THE MILITARY PAINTINGS OF
TONY JACKSON BA(Hons) Dip SIAD

A series of military *'genre'* paintings and drawings depicting the World War II experience which have been painstakingly reproduced as high quality Limited Edition, and Open Edition, fine art prints. Printed on Museum Conservation acid-free Art stock, each print off the presses has been thoroughly checked, approved, and signed personally by the artist. All prints are covered by the Publishers Guarantee, and the Limited Edition prints are signed *and* numbered and accompanied by a Certificate of Authenticity. For further details of this 'on-going' collectors series of military historical prints, a free, full colour Information Pack is available from the Publishers . . .

TONY JACKSON & ASSOCIATES
58 CLOCKTOWER PLACE, NORTH ROAD,
LONDON N7 9DY, ENGLAND
TEL: 071.609.7666   FAX: 071.607.0587

Windrow & Greene's
UK MILITARIA DIRECTORY AND SOURCEBOOK

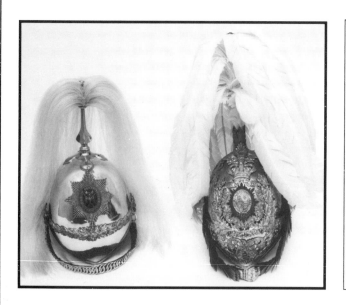

Windrow & Greene's UK MILITARIA DIRECTORY AND SOURCEBOOK

Windrow & Greene PUBLISHING

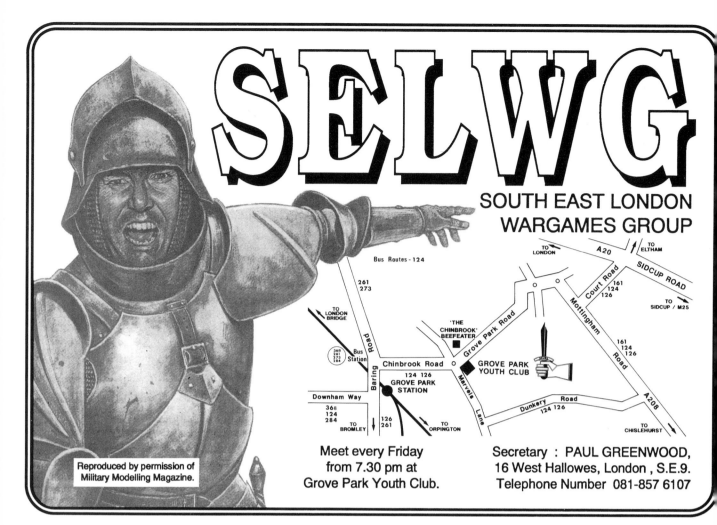

This edition first published in
Great Britain 1992 by
Windrow & Greene Ltd,
5 Gerrard Street,
London W1V 7LJ

© Windrow & Greene

ISBN 1-872004-36-9

Printed and bound in Great Britain by
Short Run Press Ltd.

CONTENTS

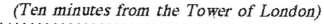

INTRODUCTION

The motivation to produce this directory came from the countless telephone calls to our office from individuals and organisations requesting information. It became clear that unlike many other hobbies and interests there was no source of reference for contacts within the militaria interest. As publishers specialising in military history, among other things, we have been on the receiving end of an amazing variety of questions; people asking where they can sell, or have valued, medals or items of military equipment; film and TV companies seeking detailed information about particular forms of military dress; those who want books, sometimes on the most obscure topics; or become a Viking at the weekends; or have a suit of armour ready-made; or sometimes just to chat about a long-dead soldier relative whose diaries may be publishable.

It may come as a surprise to some that there is such a wide-spread and growing interest in militaria and military history. Thousands of people have made a hobby of it through modelling figures or military vehicles, becoming involved in, often very authentic, historical re-enactment groups, or playing wargames. The interest forms an ideal base for the hobbyist, with mountains of complex detail and ample opportunity to follow a specialist interest into previously uncharted areas of study. Valuable research is often undertaken by amateur military historians. The hobby combines the physical detail of uniforms and weapons, from the highly elaborate to the deadly functional, the strategy of many campaigns and some of the most outstanding personalities throughout history who have been involved in war.

Why there is such a fascination with war in these so-called enlightened times is a subject for discussion elsewhere. It is a fact that as the threat of world-wide conflagration recedes the more people are fascinated by the history and detail of armed conflict.

The listings in this directory attempt to reflect the breadth of the interest. It does not pretend, and cannot hope to be comprehensive and there will inevitably be many omissions. We hope that this publication will be sufficiently successful to enable it to be published on a regular basis and that over time any omissions can be rectified. There is an entry form at the end of the book (which can be xeroxed) for those who would like to be included in the next edition to complete and return. We would appreciate any comments or suggestions from readers which we will try to incorporate into future editions. We cannot be held responsible for the information contained in this directory although every effort has been made to verify the contents.

Alan Greene
1992

Model Shops & Suppliers

Adler Miniatures
129 Bonchurch Road
Brighton
Sussex BN2 3PJ

Adventure Worlds
13 Gillingham Street
London SW1

Another World
23 Silver Street
Leicester
Leicestershire

Tel: 0533 515266

Autoroute Models
168 Bishopric
Horsham
West Sussex RH12 1QR

Avalon Hill Games
650 High Road
North Finchley
London N12 0NL

Awful Dragon Management Ltd.
3 Ransome's Dock
35–37 Parkgate Road
London SW11 4NP

B & B Miniatures
37 The Queensway
Hall Road
Hull
N. Humberside HU6 9BH

BG (GB) Models
45 Comberton Avenue
Kidderminster
Worcestershire DY10 3EQ

Tel: 0562 823829

Battle Honours
5 Moors Lane
Oreton
Nr Kidderminster
Worcs DY14 8RH

Battlefield Model Supplies
12 Delta Drive
Musselburgh
East Lothian EH21 8HR

Contact: Ian Hanratty

Tel: 031 665 4087

Mail order company specialising in A.F.V. models in plastic, resin and metal. Stock includes: Roco, Trident, M.A.A.G., C.M.S.C., Model Transport, J.B. Models, M.M.S., Trux, S & S Models, Strong-Point, Custom Miniatures. Send large s.a.e. for list.

Beatties
202 High Holborn
London WC1V 7BD

Tel: 071 405 6285
Fax: 071 405 8592

Beatties
210 Lewisham High Street
London SE13 6JP

Tel: 081 852 0449

Beatties
10 The Broadway
Southgate
London N14 6PN

Tel: 081 886 4258

Beatties
72a Broadway
West Ealing
London W13 0SY

Tel: 081 579 9959

Beatties
18/22 Market Street
Aberdeen AB1 2PL

Tel: 0224 590956

Beatties
92/94 Stamford New Road
Graftons Precinct
Altrincham WA14 1DG

Tel: 061 928 4228

Beatties
20 Chantry Way
Andover SP10 1LX

Beatties
13/15 High Street
Aylesbury HP20 1SH

Tel: 0296 85752

Beatties
21/25 Newmarket Street
Ayr KA7 1LL

Tel: 0292 282945

Beatties
28 Bridge Street
Cherwell Centre
Banbury OX16 8PN

Tel: 0295 253131

Beatties
8 New Market Square
Basingstoke RG21 1JA

Tel: 0256 59958

Beatties
26 South Mall
The Pallasades
Birmingham B2 4XD

Tel: 021 643 8604

Beatties
19 Hounds Hill Centre
Victoria Street
Blackpool FY1 4HU

Tel: 0253 26461

Beatties
16 The Concourse
Brunel Centre
Milton Keynes MK2 2HK

Tel: 0908 370478

Beatties
45 West Street
Boston
Lincs PE21 8QN

Tel: 0205 311688

Beatties
98 Poole Road
Westbourne
Bournemouth BH4 9EG

Tel: 0202 762811

Beatties
4/8 Dyke Road
Brighton BN1 3FE

Tel: 0273 776626

Beatties
17/19 Penn Street
Bristol BS1 3AW

Tel: 0272 260259

Beatties
62 Cornhill
Bury St. Edmunds JP33 1BE

Tel: 0284 761646

Beatties
Northgate House
Kingsway
Cardiff CF1 4AD

Tel: 0222 397645

Beatties
11 Britannia Way
Clyde Regional Centre
Clydebank G81 2RZ

Tel: 041 952 7368

Beatties
135a North End
Croydon CR0 1TN
Tel: 081 688 1585

Beatties
11c Forth Walk
Cumbernauld G67 1BT
Tel: 0236 734297

Beatties
7 Church Place
Dumfries DG1 1BW
Tel: 0387 64884

Beatties
8 Olympic Centre
Glasgow
Strathclyde G74 1PG
Tel: 03552 35586

Beatties
8/9 Fryern Arcade
Chandlers Ford
Eastleigh S05 2DP
Tel: 0703 269986

Beatties
30 St. Enoch Square
Glasgow G1 4DF
Tel: 041 248 6867

Beatties
24/26 Commercial Street
Halifax HX1 1TA
Tel: 0422 353986

Beatties
47/49 James Street
Harrogate HG1 1SJ
Tel: 0423 564335

Beatties
203 Marlowes
Hemel Hempstead HP1 1BL
Tel: 0442 53691

Beatties
27 White Hart Street
High Wycombe HP11 2HL
Tel: 0494 25177

Beatties
19/21 Gold Street
Newlands Centre
Kettering NN16 8BX
Tel: 0536 512507

Beatties
3/5 Bank street
Kilmarnock KA1 1HA
Tel: 0563 20262

Beatties
30/32 Eden Street
Kingston KT1 1EP
Tel: 081 549 5464

Beatties
16/18 Eden Street
Kingston KT1 1EP
Tel: 081 549 5464

Beatties
16/18 King Charles Street
Leeds LS1 6LT
Tel: 0532 456611

Beatties
36/37 Dawson Way
St John's Centre
Liverpool L1 1LJ
Tel: 051 709 0799

Beatties
6 Lords Hill Shopping Centre
Southampton SO1 8HY
Tel: 0703 737646

Beatties
4/6 Brown Street
off Market Street
Manchester M2 1EE
Tel: 061 834 7780

Beatties
64 Midsummer Arcade
Secklow Gate West
Milton Keynes MK9 3ES
Tel: 0908 604464

Beatties
25/26 Cheap Street
Newbury RG14 5DB
Tel: 0635 46004

Beatties
43/47 Pilgrim Street
Newcastle NE1 6QE
Tel: 091 232 4161

Beatties
2 High Friars
Eldon Square
Newcastle NE1 7XG
Tel: 091 261 6432

Beatties
41/43 Princes Walk
Grosvenor Centre
Northampton NN1 2EL
Tel: 0604 27726

Beatties
3 Mount Street
Nottingham NG1 6JW
Tel: 0602 411693

Beatties
15 Canal Street
Perth PH2 8LF
Tel: 0738 39450

Beatties
Unit 8
Queensgate Centre
Peterborough PE1 1NT
Tel: 0733 313158

Beatties
28 Arundel Street
Portsmouth PO1 1NL
Tel: 0705 823681

Beatties
51/52 Broad Street Mall
Shopping Centre
Reading RG1 7QE
Tel: 0734 586899

Beatties
7/11 High Street
Romford RM1 1JU
Tel: 0708 724283

Beatties
38 Pinstone Street
Sheffield S1 2HN
Tel: 0742 757864

Beatties
23 High Street
Meadowhall Shopping Centre
Sheffield S9 1EN
Tel: 0742 568267

Beatties
114 East Street
Southampton SO1 1HD
Tel: 0703 224843

Beatties
C/O Keddies Ltd.
The High Street
Southend SS1 1LA
Tel: 0702 616055

Beatties
25 Bridge Street
Swindon SN1 1BP
Tel: 0793 497213

Beatties
16 Meadway Shopping Centre
Tilehurst
Reading RG3 4AA
Tel: 0734 575571

Beatties
70 The Parade
High Street
Watford W1D 2AW
Tel: 0923 227563

Beatties
46/47 High Street
Winchester SO23 9BT

Tel: 0962 860188

Beatties
Unit 8, Caledonian Centre
New Ashtree Street
Wishaw ML2 7UR

Tel: 0698 350784

Beatties
176 Crockhamwell Road
Woodley
Reading RG5 3JH

Tel: 0734 691730

Beau Geste
121 Ipswich Road
Woodbridge
Suffolk IP12 4BY

Bicorne Miniatures
40 Church Road, Uppermill
Saddleworth
Oldham
Lancs OL3 6EL

Bob's Models
13 Oldgate
Morpeth
Northumberland

Tel: 0670 514784

Brian Sherriff Ltd.
35 Cowgate
Dundee DD1 2LW
Scotland

Contact: Managing Director

Tel: 0382 24615

Specialises in mail order military model kits. Catalogue lists over 8500 items. Accepts Visa and Mastercard orders.

Cavaliers
28 Spicer Street
St. Albans
Hertfordshire

Cheltenham Model Centre
39 High Street
Cheltenham
Gloucestershire GL50 1DY

City Models
6 Stanley Street
Liverpool
Merseyside L1 6AF

Commando
4 The Arcade
Hoe Street
London E17 4QG

Tel: 081 509 3153

Computer & Games Centre
34 St. Nicholas Cliff
Scarborough
N.Yorks YO11 2ES

Concorde Models
134 Victoria Road
Aldershot
Hampshire

Tel: 0252 26825

Condottieri
Unit 1
154 Magdalen Street
Colchester
Essex

Tel: 0206 764215

Conquest Models
11 Forresters Path
School Aycliffe
Co Durham DL5 6TA

Continental Model Supply Co
36 Gray Gardens
Rainham
Essex RM13 7NH

Custom Games
17 The Oasis
Meadowhall Shopping Centre
Sheffield
S. Yorks

C.T. Gascoigne Ltd.
101–103 Tavistock Street
Bedford
Bedfordshire

Tel: 0234 52596

Dorking Models
12–13 West Street
Dorking
Surrey RH4 1BL

Contact: Anthony Lawrence

Tel: 0306 881747

Stockists of most ranges of military kits as well as aircraft and ship models. Manufacturers of Mole military miniature white metal conversion kits in 1/35 scale. Mail order a speciality with many special imports from Eastern Europe. Open Mon–Sat (closed Wed), 9.15am–5.30pm.

Draper Models
31 Woodville Court
Roundhay
Leeds LS8 1JA

Contact: David Draper

Suppliers of painted, pewtered and unpainted figurines and associated tourist articles to museums and shops. Also sales to private collectors. Offers rental services of figures, lights, display cabinets, turntables for publicity, shows and exhibitions. Private viewing by appointment only. Colour catalogue available by post.

Drumbeat
Birmingham House
St Mary's Street
Painswick
Glos

Dumelow, A.J
70 Ferry Street
Stapenhill
Burton–on–Trent
Staffs DE15 9EY

Tel: 0283 30556

D. Hewins Models & Hobbies
7 East St. Mary's Gate
Grimsby
South Humberside DN31 1LH

Tel: Grimsby 347088

Stockists of 'Men at Arms' and many other military books and magazines. All makes of plastic kits. Wargaming and fantasy figures, plus other relevant items. General modelling and scenery accessories. Military and fantasy board/ role playing games. Open Mon–Wed Fri–Sat, 9.00am–5.30pm.

English Computer Wargames
253 Selly Oak Road
Kings Norton
Birmingham B30 1HR

Esdevium Games
2 Morley Road
Farnham
Surrey GU9 8LY

E.D. Models
64 Stratford Road
Shirley
Solihull
West Midlands B90 3LP

Tel: 021 744 7488

Fantasy and Military World
10 Market Square Arcade
Hanley
Stoke–on–Trent
Staffordshire

Tel: 0782 279294

Folio Works Ltd.
PO Box 22
Belper
Derby DE6 4HX

Fortress Models
87 Yew Tree Road
Southborough
Tunbridge Wells
Kent TN4 0BJ

Front Rank Figurines
107 Watling Street West
Towester
Northants NN12 7AG

Gallia UK
126 Buckland Way
Worcester Park
Surrey KT4 8NP

Gamers in Exile
283 Pentonville Road
London N1 9NP

Games
52 Manchester Street
Liverpool L1 6ER

Games
Unit 20
Merrion Centre
Leeds 2

Games
63 Allerton Road
Liverpool L18

Games Innovation
23 Sladesbrook
Bradford on Avon
Wilts

Games People Play
5 Wellington Terrace
Notting Hill Gate
London W2

Games Store
161 Linthorpe Road
Middlesbrough TS1 4AG

Games World
129 King Street
Hammersmith
London W6 9JG

Gaugemaster Controls
Gaugemaster House
Ford Road
Arundel
W. Sussex BN18 0BN

Tel: 0903 884321
Fax: 0903 884377

Glenmar Models & Hobbies
80 York Road
Hartlepool
Cleveland TS26 8AB

Tel: 0429 221344

Golden Gains Model Shop
7–11 Wardwick
Derby
Derbyshire DE1 1HA

Tel: 0332 44822

Grenadier Models
94 Pier Avenue
Clacton-on-Sea
Essex

Tel: 0255 421963

Hadley Hobbies
131 Middlesex Street
London E1

Tel: 071 283 9870

Helmet Soldiers
Mundy's Farm
Middle Road
Aylesbury
Bucks HP21 7AD

Contact: George Hill

Tel: 0296 415710

Manufacturer of 54mm cavalry and infantry kits. Mainly Napoleonic. Illustrated spare parts catalogues on request. Suitable for dioramas, single display figures or wargaming.

Heroes Miniatures
7 Waverley Place
Worksop
Notts S80 2SY

Historex Agents
3 Castle Street
Dover
Kent CT16 1QJ

Historical Arms
24 Winchester Road
Bishops Waltham
Hants SO3 1BD

Hoopers
105 Cornwall Street
Plymouth
Devon PL1 1PA

Contact: Brian Mardon

Tel: 0752 667840
Fax: 0752 667840

Model shop and newsagent providing selection of plastic kits, military (including naval) and transport books. Postal service.

House of Hobbies
126 High Street
Gosport
Hants PO12 1DU

Hovels
18 Glebe Road
Scartho
Grimsby
S.Humberside DN33 2HL

Howes
85 Gloucester Road
Bishopston
Bristol

Tel: 0272 247505

Imperial Figures
55a Leopold Road
Wimbledon
London SW19 7JG

Imperial War Museum
Lambeth Road
London SE1 6HZ

Contact: Linda Hart

Tel: 071 416 5000
Fax: 071 416 5374

A unique institution telling the story of 20th century warfare. It contains exhibitions on the two World Wars, a 'large exhibits' hall, art galleries, a cafe and a shop. Open Mon–Sun 10.00am–6.00pm. Admission adults £3.30, concessions £1.65. Tube Lambeth North, Elephant and Castle. British Rail – Waterloo, Elephant and Castle.

J.E. Hancock
19 Sydenham Road South
Cheltenham
Glos GL52 6EF

Keep Wargaming
The Keep, Le Marchant Bks.
London Road
Devizes
Wilts SN10 2ER

Kingsgrand Miniatures
Prinny's Gallery
The Lanes
Brighton BN1 1HB

Kohnstam, Richard
13–15 High Street
Hemel Hempstead
Herts

11

LR Models
359 Bearwood Road
Bearwood
Warley
West Midlands B66 4DB

Tel: 021 420 4332
Fax: 021 434 3043

Lamming Miniatures
21/23 Boston Road
Holbeach
Spalding
Lincs PE12 7LR

Leisure Games
91 Ballard's Lane
Finchley
London N3 1XY

Tel: 081 346 2327

Comprehensive range of brand war games, wargames rules, 'Men at Arms' reference books and minifigures. Mail order service. Send s.a.e. for list. Shop open Mon–Fri 9.30am–6.00pm, Sat 9.00am–5.30am.

Little Soldier
58 Gillygate
York
Yorkshire

Tel: 0904 642568

London Wargames Depot
56 Beaumont Place
Mogden lane
Isleworth
Middx TW7 7LH

MHW Models
46 Haworth Road
Crossroads
Keighley
West Yorks BD22 9DL

Medway Games Centre
294–6 High Street
Chatham
Kent

Tel: 0634 814750

Midland Modelcraft
70 Radnor Close
Rubery
Rednal B45 0JN

Tel: 021 453 6410

Mike's Miniatures
29 Loane Road
Sholing
Southampton S02 7PF

Tel: 0703 421956

Military Services
87 Ellacombe Road
Longwell Green
Bristol BS15 6BP

Tel: 0272 324085

Mili–Art
3 Sylverton Place
Heamoor
Nr Penzance
Cornwall

Mili–Art
18 Marine Park Mansions
Wellington Road
New Brighton
Wirral

Miniature Revolutions
44 Cheverton Avenue
Withernsea
North Humberside HU19 2HP

Mitregames
77 Burntwood Grange
Wandsworth Common
London SW18

Model Aerodrome
Unit 223
Stoneborough Centre
Maidstone
Kent

Tel: 0622 691184

Model Aerodrome
37 West Street
Brighton
E.Sussex BN1 2RE

Tel: 0273 26790

Model Aerodrome Ltd
68 Seaside Road
Eastbourne BN21 3P9

Tel: 0323 644001

Model Aerodrome Ltd.
36 The Boulevard
Crawley
Sussex RH10 1XP

Tel: 0293 540331

Model Images Retail
56 Station Road
Letchworth

Modelcraft
White Hart Mews
Southgate
Sleaford NG34 7RY

Modelkits
16 Hendford
Yeovil
Somerset

Tel: 0935 76539

Models Galore
56 London Road
Stone
Nr Dartford
Kent

Tel: 0322 278984

Models & Railways Ltd.
Unit 8, Mill Road
Fishersgate
Brighton
E.Sussex

Tel: 0273 412781

Modeltime
6 St George's Walk
Croydon CR0 1YG

Tel: 081 688 6253

Navwar
11 Electric Parade
Seven Kings Road
Ilford
Essex IG3 8BY

Contact: William McKenzie

Tel: 081 590 6731
Fax: 081 590 6731

Manufacturers of 1/1200th and 1/3000th ships, Naismith Design, Roundway Miniatures and Heroics and Ros Figures, Publishers. Complete selection of Osprey, wargame rules, paint and action zoo. Mail order specialists. Trade enquiries welcome. Open Mon–Sat (except Thurs), 9.00am–5.30pm.

Navwar
48 East View
Barnet
Herts EN5 5TN

Newark Air Museum
The Airfield
Winthorpe
Newark
Nottinghamshire NG24 2NY

Contact: Howard Heeley

Tel: 0636 707170

Located on an original bomber dispersal with nearly half of the 40 aircraft displayed undercover. Wide range of aircraft types displayed alongside aero engines, uniforms, aircraft parts, memorabilia. Admission adults £2.50, children and senior citizens £1.50.

Newbury Rules
15 Cromwell Road
Shaw
Newbury
Berks RG13 2HP

Oakmere Hobbies
161 High Street
Potters Bar
Hertfordshire

Tel: 0707 42462

Orion Models
54 Ebrington Street
Plymouth

Tel: 0752 265987

Oxford Games
6 Harper Road
Summertown
Oxford OX2 7LQ

Painted Soldiers
138 Friern Road
London SE22 OAY

Pastimes
22 Lower Park Row
Bristol
Avon 1

Patricks Toys and Models
107–111 Lillie Road
Fulham
London

Tel: 071 385 9864
Fax: 071 385 2187

Paul & Teresa Bailey
35 Long Street
Devizes
Wiltshire SN10 1NT

Pax Britannia
81 Manchester Road
Burnley
Lancs

Punctilio Model Spot
Waterloo Road
Ruby Road Corner
Hinckley
Leics LE10 0QJ

Tel: 0455 230952

Quatermasters
6 Hamilton Road
Sidcup
Kent DA15 7HB

Q.T. Models
17 Hilderthorpe Road
Bridlington
East Yorks YO15 3AY

Rank & File Models
Nine Oaks
South Hanningfield Way
Runwell, Wickford
Essex

Royal Air Force Museum
Grahame Park Way
Hendon
London NW9 5LL

Tel: 081 205 2266
Fax: 081 200 1751

National Museum of Aviation with nearly seventy aircraft. Also collections of fine art, arms and armanent, equipment, uniforms and insignia of The Royal Air Force, its predecessors and the airforces of other nations. There is also an extensive library.

Sarum Soldiers Ltd.
2a Upper Tooting Park
London SW17 7SW

Contact: Patrick Willis

Tel: 081 767 1525

Manufacturer and retailer of Sarum Studio Figurines and Sarum Traditional Soliders in 54mm scale. Studio figurines include the 'History of the Regiments' series, designed by Andrew C. Stadden. Toy soldiers include 'Armies of the Great Powers, 1870–1914', and modern British army in ceremonial uniforms.

Scale Link Co.
54 Church Street
Twickenham TW1 3NR

Tel: 081 892 1108

Schematica Software
62 Bankbottom
Hadfield
Nr Hyde
Cheshire SK15 8BY

Scorpio
20 Ordnance Row
The Hard
Portsea
Hants

Tel: 0705 830236

Scotia Micro Models
32 West Hemming Street
Letham
Angus DD8 2PU

Seafarer Books and Crafts
18 Riverside Market
Haverfordwest
Pembrokeshire SA61 2AN

Tel: 0437 768359

Second Chance Games
62 Earlston Road
Wallasey
Merseyside

Simon's Soldiers
14 Cae Ffynnon
Brackla
Bridgend
Mid. Glamorgan CF31 2HG

Skytrex Ltd
Unit 3
Canal Bank
Loughborough
Leics LE11 0HF

Soldaten
76 Fortune Green Road
London NW6 1DS

Southsea Models
69 Albert Road
Southsea
Portsmouth
Hants PO5 2SG

Space City Gifts
33 Marine Terrace
Margate
Kent CT9 1XJ

Tel: 0843 294906

Spirit Games
98/99 Horninglow Street
Burton-on-Trent
Staffs DE14 1PJ

Stamp Corner
75 Netherhall Road
Doncaster DN1 2OA

Tel: 0302 323623

Standard Games
Arion House
Station Road
Kings Langley
Herts WD4 8LF

Swansea Models & Hobbies Ltd.
30 Oxford Street
Swansea
West Glamorgan SA1 3AN

Contact: Derek Matthews

Tel: 0792 652877
Fax: 0792 652877

Stockist of military models, figure kits, paints, books, tools and equipment. One of the largest stockists of plastic kits in Wales. Open Mon–Sat, 9.00am–5.30pm. Mail order a speciality. Also stockists of conventional and fantasy wargames.

Tabletop Games
53 Mansfield Road
Daybrook
Nottingham
Notts NG5 6BB

Contact: Robert Connor

Tel: 0602 205484

Suppliers for wargamers for 15 years TTG specialise in a fast mail order service anywhere in the world. Publishers of own rules and manufacturers of figures they also supply other manufacturers products. Send s.a.e. for free mail order catalogue.

The Dragon and George
39 Parnie Street
Glasgow G1 5RJ

The Dungeon
15–17 Wine Tavern Street
Belfast BT1 1JQ

The Games Room
29A Elm Hill
Norwich
Norfolk

Tel: 0603 628140

The Guardsroom
38 West Street
Dunstable
Dunstable
Beds

Tel: 0582 606041

The Iron Duke
Edgehill Cottage
Ropeyard
Wootton Bassett
Wilts SN4 7BW

The Land of Gondal
76 Main Street
Haworth
West Yorkshire

Tel: 0535 44924

The Mad Colonel
37 Mildmay Park
Islington
London N1 4NA

Contact: Marc St. Clare

Tel: 071 354 3259

Supplier of military items from original sources. Commissions undertaken. Extensive search capability. Large network provides toy soldiers, ship and aircraft models, new and antique dinky toys. All military collectables and curios bought and sold. Write or phone with requirements.

The Model Shop
209 Deansgate
Manchester
Lancs

Tel: 061 834 3972

The Model Shop
190–194 Station Road
Harrow
London

Tel: 081 863 9788

The Model Shop
18 Blenheim Street
Newcastle Upon Tyne
Tyne & Wear NE1 4AZ

Tel: 091 232 2016

The Model Shop
179 Ferensway
Hull
North Humberside HU1 3UA

The Model Shop
22 High Street
Stroud
Gloucs GL5 1AJ

The Regiment
The Baildon Craft Centre
Browgate
Baildon
West Yorkshire

Tel: 0274 547671

The Tank Museum
Bovington Camp
Wareham
Dorset BH20 6JG

Contact: George Forty

Tel: 0929 403463
Fax: 0929 405360

Located at Bovington Camp, near Wool (British Rail), Dorset. One of the world's largest and most comprehensive armoured fighting vehicle collections. The library, photographic and plans archive is vast! The shop and mail order service sell a wide range of military books, models and model kits – send s.a.e for details. Open daily 10.00am–5.00pm except 10 days at Christmas. 1992 admission charges:– Adults £4.00, Children/OAP £2.00. Large free coach and car parks, 150 seat licensed self-service restaurant, picnic area and many other features. Regular military events held every year. A must for any modeller, wargamer and military enthusiast!

The Tin Soldier UK
31 St Pauls Road
Southsea
Hants

The Toy Soldier
16 Magdalen Street
Cambridge

Tel: 0223 67372

The Trumpet Banner
88a Sandgate High street
Folkestone
Kent CT20 3BY

Tel: 0303 220679

Tin Soldier
182 Western Road
Billericay
Essex CM12 9JD

Torbay Model Supplies Ltd.
59 Victoria Road
Ellacombe
Torquay
Devon

Tel: 0803 297764

Tradition
2 Shepherd Street
Mayfair
London W1Y 7LN

Tel: 071 493 7452
Fax: 071 355 1224

One of the longest established manufacturers and retailers in the model soldier field, its London showrooms a Mecca for many collectors. Painted and unpainted figures are available in all popular scales 54mm, 90mm and 110mm, with armies from the ancient world to the present day. Troops of the Napoleonic wars and the British army through the ages are a speciality. Also manufacturer of over 200 different toy soldier boxed sets with new releases every month, which are also available unpainted. In the smaller scales 25mm & 30mm figures are made, including the famous 'Willie' range for dioramas. Open Mon–Fri 9.00am–5.30pm, Sat 9.30am–3.00pm. Catalogues are available for all sizes.

Tradition at 10 Whitehorse Street, W.1. (071 491 7077) specialises in pre–1914 militaria including uniforms, prints and paintings. Open by appointment.

Trains & Things
170/172 Chorley New Road
Horwich
Nr Bolton
Lancs BL6 5QW

Contact: David Moss

Tel: 0204 669203

Two Dragon Productions
70 Luck Lane
Marsh
Huddersfield
West Yorks HD1 4QX

Under Two Flags
4 Saint Christopher's Place
London W1M 5HB

Contact: Jack Coutts

Tel: 071 935 6934

Stockist of toy soldiers, model kits, military books, painted figures & dioramas.   Open Mon–Sat, 10.00am–5.00pm.

Victoria Badge Company
126 Wilton Road
Victoria
London SW1

Tel: 071 834 9286

Victoriana Furnishings
88 Abbey Street
Accrington
Lancs BB5 1EB

Wargames Figures
9 Wargrave Road
Twyford
Berkshire

Warlord Games Shop
818 London Road
Leigh–on–Sea
Southend
Essex

Tel: 0702–73308

Waterloo Models
101 Eastbourne Road
Southport
Merseyside PR8 4EH

Tel: 0704 62423

Model Makers

Accurate Armour
Unit 16
Ardgowan St. Industrial Estate
Port Glasgow PA14 5DG
Scotland

Tel: 0475 43955
Fax: 0475 43746

Alban Miniatures
28 Glade Side
St. Albans AL4 9JA

Almond Sculptures Ltd.
The Nook Faussett Hill
Street End
Lower Hardres
Nr Canterbury CT4 7AJ

Tel: 0227 464424

Alternative Armies
Unit 6, Parkway Court
Glaisdale Parkway
Bilborough
Nottingham NG8 4GN

Tel: 0602 287809

Armour Models
12 Sycamore Terrace
Haswell Village
Co. Durham DH6 2AG

Contact: Paul Wade

Tel: 091 526 0485

Importers for Tonda Vac–forms, Des Kit etc. Limited supply of East European armour kits and figures. Producers of 1:35th scale resin tank crew figures. Lists available. Mail order only.

Artisan Miniatures
6 Overstone Court
Westwood
Petersborough PE3 7JE

Art of War
5 Gilson Way
Kingshurst
Birmingham B37 6BG

Contact: N.C. Mullis

Avante Garde Models
22 Barcaldine Avenue
Chryston
Glasgow G69 9NT

B & B Military
1 Kings Avenue
Ashford
Kent TN23 1LU

Tel: 0233 632923

Ballantynes of Walkerburn Ltd
Tweedale Mills (East)
Walkerburn
Borders Region EH43 6AS

Contact: Neil Ballantyne

Tel: 089687 697
Fax: 089687 409

The company sculpts, moulds, casts and despatches military and historical figures in pure pewter or cold cast bronze resin. Sold as finished (polished or painted) or in kit form. Commissions and visitors welcomed. Worldwide exports. Visa/Access accepted. Members of the Association of British Pewter Craftsmen.

Battlements
The Old Anchor of Hope
Lammas
Norwich
Norfolk NR10 5AF

Contact: Ian Weekly

Tel: 0603 279708

Known for high–quality 'one–off' model buildings in all scales for wargamers, display and museums.

Bello Wargames Figures & Accessories
88 Deerswood Court
Ifield
Crawley
West Sussex RH11 0HF

Tel: 0293 549449

Manufacturers of wargame figures in 1:200 scale (9/10mm). Range cover periods from Ancient Greeks to World War I. Send s.a.e. for free catalogue and sample figure.

Benassi's
55 St. Mungo Avenue
Glasgow G4 0PL
Scotland

Contact: Julian F. Benassi

Designer of white metal model soldiers, produced in small quantity and available by mail order. Send for catalogue.

Bombardier Models
Barton Lane Workshops
Pound Lane
Bradford on Avon
Wilts

Borbur Enterprises Limited
Unit 220
62 Tritton Road
London SE21 8DE

Tel: 081 766 7227

Border Miniatures
"Fernlea"
Penrith Road
Keswick
Cumbria CA12 4LJ

Contact: Peter Armstrong

Tel: 07687 71302

The company's white metal kits are produced and designed by Pete Armstrong. Recently, sculptor Keith Durham, has begun to produce figures for Border's 80mm series. Kits are sold by direct mail order or through specialist model shops. An illustrated catalogue is available at £1.50.

Britannia Miniatures
33 St. Mary's Road
Halton Village
Runcorn
Cheshire WA7 2BJ

Contact: David Howitt

Tel: 0928 564906

25mm wargame figures, Ancients, Colonial, Napoleonic, Crimea, Pony Wars etc. 20mm Great War, early period Germans, British and equipment. Expanding range of wargame accessories cast in resin. Mail order only. Callers by appointment. Non–illustrated listings available. Large s.a.e. required.

Caberfeidh Miniatures
Caberfeidh House
15 Church Road
Duffus
Moray IV302QQ
Scotland

Tel: 0343 830674

Campaign Figures
377 Hainton Avenue
Grimsby
South Humberside DN12 9QP

Cavendish Miniatures Ltd.
1 Little Buntings
Windsor
Berks

Tel: 0753 855474

Ceremonial Colours
A.J. Collier
3 Coppin Close
Belmont
Hereford

Ceremonial Studios
Unit 215, Victory Business Ctr
Somers Road North
Portsmouth
Hants PO1 1PJ

Chas C. Stadden Studios Ltd.
Edwin Road
Twickenham
TW2 6ST

Cheshire Volunteers
2 Brookside Road
Frodsham, WA6 7BL

Chota Sahib
124 Springfield Road
Brighton
Sussex BN1 6DE

Classic Miniatures (Scotland)
Unit 12
Currie Road Industrial Estate
Galashiels
Borders TD1 2BP

Tel: 0896 58377

Clydecast Products
97 Fereneze Avenue
Clarkston
Glasgow G76 7RT

Contact: Thomas Park

Tel: 041 638 1904

Manufacturer of model soldiers in 75, 90 and 110mm. Over 100 items produced for collectors. Mail order speciality. Also design and contract casting work undertaken. Supplies to military and Regimental museums.

Conflict Miniatures
27 Leighton Road
Harley Vale
Plymouth
Devon PL3 5RT

Tel: 0752 770761

Corvus Miniatures
Bards Hall Cottage
Chignal Smealy
Chelmsford
Essex CM1 4TL

Cromwell Models
Regency House
22 Hayburn Street
Glasgow G11 6DG

Dartmoor Military Models
Woodmanswell House
Brentor
Tavistock
Devon PL19 0NE

Tel: 0822 82 250

Davco Productions
28 Brook Street
Wymeswold
Loughborough
Leics LE12 6TU

Contact: The Managing Director

Produces an extensive range of 1/3000th scale ship models and harbour accessories for WWI, WWII and modern periods. Also produce a range of 1/300th vehicle and aircraft models for WWII and modern periods. All ranges, including new Starguard space fleet model kits, are retailed through Skytrex Ltd.

Derek Cross (AQM) Ltd.
The Old Cottage
Gilmorton
Lutterworth
Leics LE17 5PN

Contact: Derek Cross

Tel: 0455 552653
Fax: 0455 557787

Manufacturers of All The Queen's Men toy soldiers and collectors 80mm/90mm series. Colour catalogue (toy soldier) £12.00, Collectors series £6.00 (b/white). Viewing by appointment only, Mon-Sat. World wide mail order.

Dixon Miniatures
Spring Grove Mills
Linthwaite
Huddersfield
W Yorkshire

Tel: 0484 846162

Donnington Miniatures
15 Cromwell Road
Shaw
Newbury
Berkshire RG13 2HP

Draper Models
31 Woodville Court
Roundhay
Leeds LS8 1JA

Contact: David Draper

Suppliers of painted, pewtered and unpainted figurines and associated tourist articles to museums and shops. Also sales to private collectors. Offers rental services of figures, lights, display cabinets, turntables for publicity, shows and exhibitions. Private viewing by appointment only. Colour catalogue available by post.

Drumbeat
Birmingham House
St Mary's St
Painswick
Gloucestershire

Ducal Models
Fort Ducal
Eastleigh SO5 6HQ

Tel: 0703 692119

D.F. Grieve Models
Westwood Road
Betsham
Nr Gravesend
Kent DA13 9LZ

Fax: 05/03/91

D.M.H. Models
3 Greensand Road
Bearsted
Maidstone
Kent ME15 8NY

Contact: Derek Hanson

Tel: 0622 39186

Miniature figure designer and manufacturer.

Eagle Miniatures
Wild Acre
Minchinhampton
Glos GL6 9AJ

Contact: David Atkins

Tel: 0453 835782

Design, manufacture and distribute 15mm, 25mm and 54mm figures from the Seven Years, Napoleonic and American Civil War. A 'design and cast' service is available. Call by appointment. Occasionally hosts megagames.

Ensign Miniatures
Littlebury Hall
Station Road
Kirton, Boston
Lincolnshire PE20 LQ

Contact: Robert & Ann Rowe

Tel: 0205 722101

Specialises in high quality 54mm metal figures. Illustrated catalogue of 250 figures, contains mess dress, naval, undress, Napleonic, European, A.C.W. and knights. World wide mail order service. Callers welcome.

Euro-Militaire
Unit 3
69 Weyhill Road
Andover
Hants

Tel: 0264 333470
Fax: 0264 334120

Fire Force Products
Unit 26, Supa Shopper
27-28 High St
Kings Heath
Birmingham B14 7LB

Fort Royal Review
25 Woolhope Road
Worcester WR5 2AR

Tel: 0905 356379

Fort Royal Review
65 Drovers Way
Astwood Farm
Worcester WR3 8QD

Fortress Models
87 Yew Tree Road
Southborough
Tunbridge Wells
Kent TN4 0BJ

Front Rank Figurines
11 Southbourne Gardens
Westcliff-on-Sea
Essex SS0 0AG

Front Rank Figurines
107 Watling Street West
Towcester
Northants NN12 7AG

Geo. W. Neale Ltd
Victoria Road
London NW10 6NG

Tel: 081 965 1336

Good Soldiers
246 Broadwater Crescent
Stevenage
Herts SG2 8HC

Hart Models
13 Hunts Common
Hartley Wintney
Hampshire RG27 8NT

Tel: 025 126 2637

Haselup, Gavin
Kennel House
150 Cape House, Capel-le-Ferne
Folkestone
Kent CT18 7HA

Heco
23 Addison Road
Brockenhurst
Hampshire SO4 27SD

Helmet Soldiers
Munday's Farm
Middle Road
Aylesbury
Bucks HP21 7AD

Heroics & Ros Figures
Unit 12 Semington Turnpike
Semington
Trowbridge
Wilts BA14 6LB

Tel: 0380 870228
Fax: 0380 871045

Highlander Miniatures
47 Spruce Armington
Tamsworth
Staffs

History in Procelain
High Street
Shoreham
Kent TN14 7TD

Tel: 09592 3416

Hornet Models
PO Box 64
Rochester
Kent ME1 3JR

Contact: Nicholas Adams

A range of true 1/35 scale metal figures for the collector and diorama builder. Both WWII and modern figures and accessories (ranging from seperate heads, arm packs, and weapons for kits of bicycles, airborne scooters, and small anti-tank guns) available by mail order. Send s.a.e. for sales sheet.

Howes
85 Gloucester Road
Bishopston
Bristol

Tel: 0272 247505

Hussar Military Miniatures
177 Boston Road
Hanwell
London W7 2HR

Tel: 081 579 4457

Ian White Models
238 Taunton Avenue
Whitleigh
Plymouth
Devon PL5 4EW

Tel: 0752 768507

Invicta Figures
43 Bow Road
Wateringbury
Kent ME18 5DA

Jacobite Miniatures Ltd.
65 Byfield Road
Woodfield Halse
Nr Daventry
Northants

Kingscast
Unit 9, Industrial Estate
Presteigne
Powys LD8 2UG
Wales

Tel: 0544 260130

Kingfisher Design
The Old Barn
19 Fry's Lane
Everton
Lymington
Hants SO41 0JY

Laing, Peter
Minden
Sutton St. Nicholas
Hereford HR1 3BD

Lancashire Games (Mail Order)
20 Platting Road
Lydgate
Oldham
Lancs OL4 4DL

Contact: Allan Lumley

Tel: 0497 872212

Offers a range of miniatures from Renaissance to Colonial in 15mm, main ranges are horse and musket periods (Seven Years War to American Civil War). Painting service available on own range of miniatures and most other popular manufacturers. Send s.a.e. for full lists.

Langley Models
166 Three Bridges Road
Crawley
Sussex RH10 1LE

Tel: 0293 516329
Fax: 0293 616955

Lead Sled Models
Unit 3, Round House Craft Ctr
Buckland in the Moor
Ashburton
Devon TQ13 7HN

Tel: 0364 52971

Long Range Logistics
41 Whorlton Road
Stockton on Tees
Cleveland TS19 8NH

Contact: Garry Harbottle-Johnson

Tel: 0642 670107

Mail order and wargames show trader. Specialist in 20th century 6mm models, also 6mm science fiction, rules and scenics for all periods (ancient – science fiction) in all scales. Rules and army list authors/ publishers and specialist stockist of 6mm aircraft. Callers by appointment only.

MLR Figures
111 Geere Road
London E15 3PP

MLR Figures
17 Oakfield Drive
Upton Heath
Chester CH2 1LG

MMS Models
26 Crescent Rise
Luton
Beds LU2 0AU

Marlborough Military Models
The Duchy
Pontycymmer
Brigend CF32 8DU

Tel: 0656 871774

Matchlock Miniatures
26 Cliffsea Grove
Leigh-on-Sea
Essex SS9 1NQ

McCann, D.
218 Fen Road
RAF Marham
Kings Lynn
Norfolk PE33 9NP

Mick Lunn Metal Masters
46 Staindale Guisborough
Cleveland TS14 8JU

Tel: 0287 52760

Mike French Models
19 Langton Road
Boscombe
Bournemouth
Dorset BH7 6HS

Mike Papworth Miniatures
36 Rosedale Road
Kingsthorpe
Northampton

Mil Art
41 Larksfield Crescent
Dovercourt
Harwich
Essex CO12 4BJ

Milestone Sculpture Design
10 Portland Street
Blyth
Northumberland NE24 1NP

Contact: Peter Miles

Tel: 0670 560866

Milicast
P.O. Box 711
Glasgow G41 2HX

Contact: Tom Welsh

Manufacturers of authentic scale model military kits in 1:76 scale in polyurethane resin. Over 100 kits in the range. Also specialise in all WWII A.F.V's, 'Soft-skin' tanks, armoured landing vehicles etc.. Send s.a.e for free catalogue. Mail order.

Military Pageant
45 Silverston Way
Stanmore
Middx HA7 4HS

Miniature Military Models
302 London Road
Stretton-on-Dunsmore
Rugby
Warwickshire CV23 9HX

Contact: William Bowden

Tel: 0203 543451

Model figure, vignette and dioramic scene maker. Most work carried out in small scale 54–75mm. All work is presented mounted on wooden bases. Quotations given upon request.

Mitrecap Miniatures
Manorfield House
46 Main Street
Ashton-c-Aughtn
Sheffield S31 0XJ

Model Figures & Hobbies
4 Lower Balloo Road
Groomsport
Co. Down BT19 2LU

Contact: Norman Robinson

Tel: 0247 883187

Manufacturer of Platoon 20 WWII and modern wargame figures and equipment. Also Ensign 1/1200 scale model ships and aircraft and the Plastiform scenics range of Vacforms.

Mr Thompson
26 Glade Road
Marlow
Bucks SL7 1DY

M.C. Export and Enterprises
The Flat, Shadowlawn
Kimcote
Lutterworth
Leics LR17 5RU

Tel: 045 55 3430

Navwar
11 Electric Parade
Seven Kings Road
Ilford
Essex IG3 8BY

Contact: William McKenzie

Tel: 081 590 6731
Fax: 081 590 6731

Manufacturers of 1/1200th and 1/3000th ships, Naismith Design, Roundway Miniatures and Heroics and Ros Figures, Publishers. Complete selection of Osprey, wargame rules, paint and action zoo. Mail order specialists. Trade enquiries welcome. Open Mon-Sat (except Thurs), 9.00am–5.30pm.

New Hope Designs
Tynewald Mills
St.John's
Isle of Man

Contact: David Winter

Tel: 0624 801529
Fax: 0624 801623

Produces more than one thousand white metal figure kits. Founded in 1973, the majority of the company's products are based on the full colour artwork which appears in the Osprey Publishing series of Men-at-Arms and Elite titles. A comprehensive listing/catalogue is available on request.

Also see colour advertisement.

Nik Studios
49 The Meads
Edgeware
Middx

Tel: 081 959 5289

Nik Studio's
38 Northfield Road
New Barnet
Herts EN4 9DN

Tel: 081 441 3226

North West Frontier
61 Trafalgar Road
Bowerham
Lancaster
Lancs LA1 4DB

On Guard Miniatures
22 Maudlin Street
Hetton-le-Hole
Tyne & Wear DH5 9BG

Phina Figures
106 Cowley Road
Mortlake
London SW14 8QB

Contact: Philip Orr

Tel: 081 876 0006

Manufacturer of detailed action figures. Also freelance miniature sculpting and casting service. 54mm series include: American Civil War, Marlborough Armies and English Civil War. Spare packs include heads, weapons and equipment. 90mm Heros of the Alamo. Send s.a.e. for information.

Phoenix Model Developments Ltd.
Earl Barton
Northampton NN6 0NA

Tel: Nrthmpton 810612

Piper Craft
4 Hillside Cottages
Glenboig
Lanarkshire ML5 2QY

Contact: Thomas Moles

Tel: 0236 873801
Fax: 0236 873044

Manufacturer of white metal military and non–military figures designed to a general scale of 75mm 93". Suppliers to museums, places of historic interest, shops and collectors. Established 1985. Send s.a.e. or 2 x IRC's for a complete illustrated list.

Platoon 20
Lower Balloo Road
Groomsport
Co. Down BT23 3QZ

Positive Figurines
52 Donellan Green
Southfields
Northampton
Northamptonshire NN3 5DJ

Contact: David Maguire

Tel: 0604 644829

Manufacturer and mail order supplier of own general range of 54mm–90mm model soldiers. Illustrated catalogue 90p, price list s.a.e. or 2 IRC's.

Present Arms
5 Holmfirth Close
Belmont
Hereford HR2 7UG

Tel: 0432 276510

Prince August UK
Dept 8M
Small Dole
Henfield
Sussex BN5 9XH

Pro Mods
Suite 2, Wincombe Trading Est
Albert Road
Bristol BS2 0XW

Tel: 0272 724433

Punctilio Model Spot
Waterloo Road
Ruby Road Corner
Hinckley
Leics LE10 0QJ

Tel: 0455 230952

RHQ R.Irish
5 Waring Street
Belfast BT1 2EW

Raventhorpe Miniatures
2 Bygot Lane
Cherry Burton
Beverley
Humberside HU17 7RN

Contact: Anthony Chadburn

Tel: 0964 551027

20mm WWI and WWII specialist mail order. Send s.a.e. and 2 x 1st class stamps for catalogue.

Redoubt Enterprises
49 Channel View Road
Eastbourne
East Sussex BN22 7LN

Regimental Statuette Manufactuers
Littlebury Hall
Station Road, Kirton
Nr. Boston
Lincolnshire PE20 1LQ

Contact: Robert and Ann Rowe

Tel: 0205 722101

Family business providing limited edition, large scale (11" approx), high quality statuettes primarily for military establishments. Figures are cast in resin with white metal parts and finished either in bronze or are hand painted. Callers welcomed to discuss requirements.

Reheat Models
1a Oak Drive
North Bradley
Trowbridge
Wiltshire BA14 0SW

Richard Newth–Gibbs Painting Services
59 Victor Close
Hornchurch
Essex RM12 4XH

Tel: 04024 48785

15mm to any scale, single figures, groups, dioramas, artillery pieces, mounted gun teams, British and Indian army specialist. Factual military work only. Callers by appointment.

Robinson Imports
25 Princetown Road
Bangor
Co. Down BT20 3TA

Contact: Cameron Robinson

Tel: 0247 472860

Importer of Italian model figure range Mirliton S.G. 25mm, Ancient, Medieval, Renaissance, French Revolutionary, Napoleonic Wars, Italian War of Independence 1859. Also available 'Empire, Eagles & Lions' Napoleonic wargames magazine.

Rosedale Figurines
8 China Street
Lancaster
Lancs LA1 1EX

Tel: 0524 65129

Sahib, Chota
124 Springfield Road
Brighton BN1 6DE

Sarum Soldiers
2a Upper Tooting Park
London SW17 7SW

Scale Link Co.
54 Church Street
Twickenham TW1 3NR

Tel: 081 892 1108

Scorpio
20 Ordnance Row
The Hard
Portsea
Hants

Tel: 0705 830236

Shetland Isles Toy & Model Soldier Co.
32 Toll Clock Shopping Centre
26 North Road
Lerwick
Shetland ZE1 0PE

Sovereign Miniatures
4 Hawbeck Road
Gillingham
Kent

Spartan Studio
26 Majors Close
Chedburgh
Bury St Edmunds
Suffolk IP29 4UN

Tel: 0284 850326

Steadfast Soldiers
Unit 22
62 Tritton Road
London SE21 8DE

Tel: 081 766 7227

Stuart West Figures
74 Rotherham Road
Holbrooks
Coventry
West Midlands CV6 4FE

Contact: Stuart West

Tel: 0203 666376

Specialises in white metal and resin figures from 54mm, 90mm and 120mm. Also suppliers of original hand painted toy soldiers in boxed sets. Full painting service is also available in all scales. Mail order service only and can supply to the trade.

Syntown Miniatures
Knellstone Lodge
Udimore
Nr Rye
E.Sussex TN31 6AR

TV Models
147 Fauldsgate
Aberdeen AB1 5RB
Scotland

The Drum
107 Watling Street West
Towcester
Northants NN12 7AG

Contact: Michael Green

Tel: 0327 359276
Fax: 0327 50435

Stockists of wargames figures and boardgames, fantasy & sci-fi roleplaying games and mail order service. Manufacturers of resin buildings and accessories for the wargaming and role playing hobbies. Open Mon–Thur 9.30am–5.30pm, Fri & Sat 9.30am–6.00pm. Send s.a.e. for resin castings catalogue.

The Elite Collection
Bank House
127 High Street
Crediton
Devon EX17 3LQ

Tel: 0395 273126

The Lancaster Collection
20 Clarendon Road
Tonse Fold
Bolton BL2 6BT

The Last Outpost
85 Kentmere Crescent
Leeds LS14 1JR

The Last Outpost
Unit 13
30–38 Dock Street
Leeds LS10 1JF

The Miniature Architect
23 Wylam Street
Craghead
Stanley
Co. Durham DH9 6ER

Contact: Andrew Copestake

Tel: 283332

Maker of high quality handbuilt model buildings and fortification in all scales from 1/300–1/32 for the discerning collector, or wargamer. May be purchased from their "off the peg" list or specially commissioned to customer requirements. From single models to cities, from log cabins to castles, dioramas and landscapes also constructed and painted to customer specification in any scale 1/300–1/32. Write with s.a.e. or 2 IRC stating interests or requirements. Personal callers by prior arrangement only.

The Trumpet Banner
88a Sandgate High street
Folkestone
Kent CT20 3BY

Tel: 0303 220679

Thistle Miniatures
Findon Croft
Findon
Aberdeen AB1 4RN

Contact: Managing Director

Tel: 0224 571831

Manufacturer of white metal/resin figures in 1/24th, 1/20th and 1/16th scales. They are mainly Scottish, in ranges; modern barrack dress, The Great War, personalities, and mess dress. Prints depicting the kilts and trews of the British army. All these available by mail or telephone order.

Tiny Troopers
13 Leaphill Road
Portsmouth BH7 6L5

Tel: 0202 394514

Tradition
2 Shepherd Street
Mayfair
London W1Y 7LN

Tel: 071 493 7452
Fax: 071 355 1224

One of the longest established manufacturers and retailers in the model soldier field, its London showrooms a Mecca for many collectors. Painted and unpainted figures are available in all popular scales 54mm, 90mm and 110mm, with armies from the ancient world to the present day. Troops of the Napoleonic wars and the British army through the ages are a speciality. Also manufacturer of over 200 different toy soldier boxed sets with new releases every month, which are also available unpainted. In the smaller scales 25mm & 30mm figures are made, including the famous 'Willie' range for dioramas. Open Mon–Fri 9.00am–5.30pm, Sat 9.30am–3.00pm. Catalogues are available for all sizes.

Tradition at 10 Whitehorse Street, W.1. (071 491 7077) specialises in pre–1914 militaria including uniforms, prints and paintings. Open by appointment.

Trophy Miniatures Wales Ltd
Unit 10, Barry Workshops
Sully Moors Road
Sully, Penarth
South Glamorgan CF6 2XB

Tel: 0446 721011
Fax: 0446 732483

Trux Models
156 High Street
Yeadon
Leeds LS19 7AB

Contact: Mike Simpson

Tel: 0532 502051

Manufacturers of 1/76 scale kits in polyurethane resin specialising in wheeled vehicles used by the British Army in WWII. Also publish sets of factsheets on the organisation and vehicles used in various campaigns. Mail order only. Quarterly list on receipt of s.a.e..

Tyresmoke Products
21 Brampton Court
Bowershill
Melksham SN12 6TH

Viking Miniatures Ltd
Littlebury Hall
Station Road
Kirton, Nr Boston
Lincolnshire PE20 1LQ

Vintage Ltd
104 Stanwell Road
Penarth
South Glamorgan CF6 2LP

Contact: David Vanner

Tel: 0222–701030

International mail order metal waterline
model ship business established for 12
years. Regular stands taken at collector's
meetings. For illustrated lists of stocks
and shows send £1.00 plus s.a.e..

Wacker, I.
900 Rutherglen Road
Glasgow

Wargames Foundry
4a Parkyn Road
Daybrook
Nottingham NG5 6BG

Tel: 0602 260163

Wargames South
24 Cricketers Close
Ockley
Surrey RH5 5BA

Welsh Dragon Miniatures
Ty Newydd Nebo Caernarfon
Gwynedd LL54 6EL

Western Miniatures
127 Merlin Way
Chipping Sodbury
Bristol

Wild Geese Miniatures
35 Cross Street
Upton
Pontefract
West Yorkshire WF9 1EU

Model Equipment & Services

Alec Tiranti Ltd.
70 High Street
Theale
Reading
Berks RG7 5AR

Contact: Managing Director

Tel: 0734 302487

Sculptors' tools, materials and equipment, including silicone rubbers, white metals, centricast machines, ceramic shell lost wax casting kits (Reid technique), fine modelling tools and materials, Milliput. London branch: 27 Warren Street, W1 (071 636 8565), open Mon–Fri 9am–5.30pm, Sat 9.30am–1.00pm. Theale Mon–Fri 8.30am–5.00pm, Sat 9.30am–1.00pm (mail order). Access and Visa.

See advetisement in this section.

Applied Plymer Systems
Westburn House
Parish Ghyll Road
Ilkley
Yorkshire LS29 9NG

Argus Adhesive Service
Argus House
Boundary Way
Hemel Hempstead HP2 7ST

Tel: 0442 66551
Fax: 0442 66998

Art of War
5 Gilson Way
Kingshurst
Birmingham B37 6BG

Tel: 021 749 5676

Awful Dragon Management Ltd.
3 Ransome's Dock
35–37 Parkgate Road
London SW11 4NP

Battle Art
13 Cameron Drive
Auchin Leck
Ayreshire KA18 2JE

Battleground Miniatures
94 Westwood Road
Sutton Coldfield
Birmingham B73 6UJ

Tel: 021 353 3218

Beatties
See full listing under Model Shops.

Bonaparte's
11 Friars Close
Dilton Marsh
Westbury
Wilts BA13 4BS

Tel: 0373 823955

Bryce
52 Caradoc Street
Taibach
Port Talbot
West Glamorgan

Bugle & Musket
148 Valley Crescent
Wrenthorpe
Wakefield
Yorkshire WF2 0ND

Burrell, Len
308 Church Road
Kessingland Beach
Loewstoft
Suffolk NR33 7SB

Cannons, R.A.
The Old Stores
Kingscott, St Giles in the Wood
Torrington
Devon EX38 7JW

Tel: 0805 23816

Manufacturers of display units.

Capital Model Supplies
42 Anerley Hill
London SE19 2AE

Carn Metals Ltd.
8 Carn View Terrace
Pendeen
Cornwall TR19 7DU

Contact: Managing Director

Tel: 0736 787343

Manufacturer of high quality pewters, whitemetal casting alloys and solders from 250gms to 250kg.

Charles Frank Ltd.
Ronald Lane
Carlton Park
Saxmundham
Suffolk IP17 2NL

Tel: 0728 603506

Coker Bros. Ltd.
Unit 5
Upper Brents Industrial Estate
Faversham
Kent ME13 7DZ

Tel: 0795 535008
Fax: 0795 532146

Collector Cabinets
Eastburn House
Green Lane
Eastburn
Nr Keighly BD20 8UT

Tel: 0535 656030

Craft Supplies
Millers Dale
Buxton
Derbys SK17 8SN

Tel: 0298 871636

Cross's
119 Sandgate Road
Folkestone
Kent CT20 2BL

Tel: 0303 52391

C.R. Clarke & Co (UK) Ltd.
Unit 3
Betws Industrial Park
Ammanford
Dyfed SA18 2LS

Contact: Christopher Clarke

Tel: 0269 593860
Fax: 0269 591890

D & A Hobbies
31 Brierley Road
Henley Green
Coventry CV2 1RS

Tel: 0203 621248

DCS
209b The Big Peg
Vyse Street, Hockley
Birmingham B18 6NF

Tel: 021 212 1538

DKL Metals Ltd.
Avontoun Works
Linlithgow EH49 6QD

Tel: 0506 847710

Davco Productions
28 Brook Street
Wymeswold
Loughborough
Leics LE12 6TU

Contact: The Managing Director

Produces an extensive range of 1/3000th scale ship models and harbour accessories for WWI, WWII and modern periods. Also produce a range of 1/300th vehicle and aircraft models for WWII and modern periods. All ranges, including new Starguard space fleet model kits, are retailed through Skytrex Ltd..

Daylight Studios
223a Portobello Road
London W11 1LU

Contact: Suzanne Graff

Tel: 071 229 7812
Fax: 071 727 1773

Daylight lighting specialists supplying 60, 75 and 100 watt daylight simulation bulbs. Also stocks 150 watt daylight simulation bulbs, daylight spotlights, 100 watt clip–on lights. Send s.a.e. for free colour catalogue.

Dorking Models
12–13 West Street
Dorking
Surrey RH4 1BL

Contact: Anthony Lawrence

Tel: 0306 881747

Stockists of most ranges of military kits as well as aircraft and ship models. Manufacturers of Mole military miniature white metal conversion kits in 1/35 scale. Mail order a speciality with many special imports from Eastern Europe. Open Mon–Sat (closed Wed), 9.15am–5.30pm.

D. Hewins Models & Hobbies
7 East St. Mary's Gate
Grimsby
South Humberside DN31 1LH

Tel: Grimsby 347088

Stockists of 'Men at Arms' and many other military books and magazines. All makes of plastic kits. Wargaming and fantasy figures, plus other relevant items. General modelling and scenery accessories. Military and fantasy board/ role playing games. Open Mon–Wed Fri–Sat, 9.00am–5.30pm.

D.R. Models
47 Glebe Road
Ampthill
Bedfordshire MK45 2TJ

Tel: 0525 840140

Eagle Miniatures
Wild Acre
Minchinhampton
Glos GL6 9AJ

Contact: David Atkins

Tel: 0453 835782

Design, manufacture and distribute 15mm, 25mm and 54mm figures from the Seven Years, Napoleonic and American Civil War. A 'design and cast' service is available. Call by appointment. Occasionally hosts megagames.

Fine Art Castings & Machinery
Unit 3
Weyhill Road
Andover
Hants

Tel: 0264 333470
Fax: 0264 334120 F

Flapstock Ltd.
Shucklow Building
Little Horwood
Milton Keynes
Bucks MK17 0PT

Contact: Vivian Wilson

Tel: 0296 713631
Fax: 0296 714155

Suppliers of white metal casting alloys including pewter, kax, 34%, 37/3/60 and D alloy. Also low melt solder and flux. Suppliers of casting equipment and model making metals. Send for catalogue (Dept WG).

Formation Plastix
Unit E4
Hilton Main Business Park
Featherstone
Staffs WV10 7HP

Tel: 0902 723999

Frei–Korps 15
25 Princetown Road
Bangor
Co. Down BT20 3TA

Contact: Cameron Robinson

Tel: 0247 472860

Large range of 15mm scale wargame figures. Publisher of a series of military campaign books and rules. Periods covered included Ancient, Thirty Years War, Seven Years War, American Wars 1774–1880's, British in India, Europe 1850–1870 and artillery.

GJM Figurines
24 Chelsfield Mews
Stanton Close
Orpington
Kent BR5 4RN

Tel: 0689 820115

Gedemco
163 Reddish Road
South Reddish
Stockport
Cheshire SK5 7HP

Tel: 061 477 9352

Gildea, Brian A.
83 Parham Road
Gosport
Hants PO12 4UA

Graphic Air Systems
8 Cold Bath Road
Harrogate
Nrth Yorkshire HG2 0NA

Historex Agents
3 Castle Street
Dover
Kent CT16 1QJ

Humbrol Ltd.
Marfleet
Hull
Nth Humberside HU9 5NE

Tel: 0482 701191
Fax: 0482 712908

Ian Overton
133 Parklands Drive
Loughborough
Leicestershire LE11 2TA

Tel: 0509 231489

Kingkit
6 Broadway
Shifnal
Shropshire TF11 8AZ

Contact: Malcolm Rolling

Tel: 0952 460587

Kit search specialist. Catalogues available by subscription. Primarily mail order (worldwide). Shop open Sat only, 10.00am–5.00pm.

Laing, John
70 Harcourt Street
Newark
Notts NG24 1RF

Lancashire Games (Mail Order)
20 Platting Road
Lydgate
Oldham
Lancs OL4 4DL

Contact: Allan Lumley

Tel: 0497 872212

Offers a range of miniatures from Renaissance to Colonial in 15mm, main ranges are horse and musket periods (Seven Years War to American Civil War). Painting service available on own range of miniatures and most other popular manufacturers. Send s.a.e. for full lists.

Linka
Alnwick Station
Alnwick
Northumberland NE66 2NP

Tel: 0665 604888

Long Range Logistics
41 Whorlton Road
Stockton on Tees
Cleveland TS19 8NH

Contact: Garry Harbottle–Johnson

Tel: 0642 670107

Mail order and wargames show trader. Specialist in 20th century 6mm models, also 6mm science fiction, rules and scenics for all periods (ancient – science fiction) in all scales. Rules and army list authors/publishers and specialist stockist of 6mm aircraft. Callers by appointment only.

MR Pictures Ltd.
Claire Road
Kirby Cross
Essex CO13 0LY

Tel: 0255 850974
Fax: 0255 678534

Mac Warren
50 Sunnybank
Hull HU3 1LQ

Tel: 0482 48704

Minicraft
Westpoint
The Grove
Slough
Berkshire SL1 1QQ

Model Figures & Hobbies
4 Lower Balloo Road
Groomsport
Co. Down BT19 2LU

Contact: Norman Robinson

Tel: 0247 883187

Manufacturer of Platoon 20 WWII and modern wargame figures and equipment. Also Ensign 1/1200 scale model ships and aircraft and the Plastiform scenics range of Vacforms.

Oakwood Studios
17 Birkhill Crescent
Birkenshaw
Nr Bradford
West Yorkshire BD11 2LJ

Contact: William R Mortimer

Tel: 0532 853234

Produces hardwood bases for the military modelling enthusiast. Offers a list of 65 sixes in yew and mahogany including plinth bases. Made to measure service to modellers own drawings and a choice of exotic woods. Mail order only.

Paintworks
93 Kingsland Road
London E2 8AG

Tel: 071 729 7451

Stocks comprehensive range of art materials for model makers. Rembrandt oils and acrylics, Peukan Plaka, sable and synthetic spotters etc. Send s.a.e. for mail order price list. Open Tues– Sat 9.30am–5.30pm (Fri to 7.00pm).

Picturesque
25/27 Tufton Street
Ashford
Kent TM23 1QN

Tel: 0233 641682

Proops Bros Ltd.
21 Masons Avenue
Harrow
Middx HA3 5AH

Contact: David Proops

Tel: 081 861 5258
Fax: 081 861 5404

Full range of miniature and precision hand tools, cutting mats, illuminated bench magnifier, Bager air brushes, minicraft and a complete selection of miniature lamps and switches. Send £2.00 for catalogue.

Proops Brothers Ltd.
Technology House
34 Saddington Road
Fleckney
Leicester LE8 0AW

Rawson, M.
82 Greenvale Road
London SE9 1PD

Contact: M Rawson

Richard Kernick
Wrecclesham Road
Farnham
Surrey GU10 4PS

Tel: 0252 733255

Robinson Imports
25 Princetown Road
Bangor
Co. Down BT20 3TA

Contact: Cameron Robinson

Tel: 0247 472860

Importer of Italian model figure range Mirliton S.G. 25mm, Ancient, Medieval, Renaissance, French Revolutionary, Napoleonic Wars, Italian War of Independence 1859. Also available 'Empire, Eagles & Lions' Napoleonic wargames magazine.

Rose Paints
Ceremonial Studios
88 Orchard Road
Southsea
Hants PO4 0AB

Tel: 0705 732753

Rotring/Conopois Airbrush & Spray Centre
39 Littlehampton Road
Worthing
West Sussex BN13 1QJ

Contact: Kenneth Medwell

Tel: 0903 66991
Fax: 0903 830045

Airbrush and compressor equipment and materials suppliers. Main agents for Iwata and Paasche, including own manufactured products. Extensive range of equipment backed up with airbrush advice line and own workshops. Servicing, repairs and spares available on most major makes of equipment by factory trained staff. Industrial spray equipment also available.

Set Scenes
PO Box 63
Crawley
West Sussex RH11 8YR

Stauve Galleries
34 Lower Street
Dartmouth
Devon TQ6 9AN

Tel: 0803 835020

Sungro-lite Ltd.
118 Chatsworth Road
London NW2 5QU

Tel: 081 459 2636
Fax: 081 459 4130

"Natural" light bulbs – true colour rendition, cool, glare–free diffused light. Similar to indirect sunlight for model making and painting. Available in 75/100/150 watt. Mail order service available. No callers without appointments. Phone or write for details or order form.

S.V.F.
Unit 14d
Whitebridge Industrial Estate
Stone
Staffordshire

Tel: 0785 814654

The Colour Sergeant
4 Sandhurst Crescent
Leigh-on-Sea
Essex SS9 4AL

The Dreamsmith
13 Church Lane
Killamarsh
Sheffield S31 8AS

Contact: Nick Reynolds

Tel: 0742 483124

The Fife and Drum
479 Heather Path
Collydean
Glenrothes
Fife KY7 6TX

Tel: 0592 745377

The Last Detail
196 Parlaunt Road
Langley
Slough
Berkshire SL3 8AZ

The Mad Colonel
37 Mildmay Park
Islington
London N1 4NA

Contact: Marc St. Clare

Tel: 071 354 3259

Supplier of military items from original sources. Commissions undertaken. Extensive search capability. Large network provides toy soldiers, ship and aircraft models, new and antique dinky toys. All military collectables and curios bought and sold. Write or phone with requirements.

Toyway
PO Box 55, Unit 20
Jubilee Trade Cntr, Jubilee Rd
Letchworth
Herts SG6 1SG

Contact: Richard Morriss

Tel: 0462 672509
Fax: 0462 672132

Trains & Things
170/172 Chorley New Road
Horwich
Nr Bolton
Lancs BL6 5QW

Contact: David Moss

Tel: 0204 669203

Virgin Soldiers
81 Coleridge Road
Weston–Super–Mare
Avon BS23 3UJ

Tel: 0934 614153

Wilson, R.
307 Nottingham Road
Ikeston
Derbyshire DE7 5BB

Wiremill Turning
Four Crosses, Wiremill Lane
Newchapel
Lingfield
Surrey RH7 6HJ

Tel: 0342 834918

Model Societies

Avon International Plastic Modelling Soc
Bath Pavillion
North Parade
Bath
Avon

Tel: 0272 422813

BMSS Bristol Branch
Old Coach House
18 York Place, Clifton
Bristol BS8 1AH

Tel: 0272 732067

BMSS Herts Branch
96 High Avenue
Letchworth
Herts SG6 3RR

Tel: 0462 676020

British Flat Figure Society
23 Glastonbury Court
Talbot Rd
London W13 0SL

British Model Soldier Society
c/o 22 Lynwood Road
Ealing
London W5 1JJ

Contact: David Pearce

Tel: 081 998 5230

Founded in 1935 and caters for the interests of the modeller and collector. Over 20 branches and members in 20 countries are kept in touch by magazine, newsletters and branch open days. Competitions and auctions take place regularly,

See advertisement. in this section

City & East London Model Making Club
St John Ambulance Hall
East Avenue, Walthamstow
London E17

Contact: Paul Melton

Tel: 081 559 0189 (pm)

Colchester Military Modelling Soc
97 Shelley Road
Colchester
Essex CM2 6ES

Contact: Tony Surridge

Tel: 0245 281878

Meetings fortnightly (Thurs). Caters for all types of modeller.

Darlington Military Modelling
127 Dinsdale Crescent
Darlington
Co Durham DL1 1EZ

Tel: 0325 489801

Dorset BMSS
21 Whitecliff
Mill Street
Blandford
Dorset

Tel: 0258 454626

Halesowen Military Modelling
45 Comberton Avenue
Kidderminster
Worcs DY10 3EQ

Tel: 0562 823829

International Plastic Modellers Society
9 Pretoria Road
Gillingham
Kent ME7 4ND

Contact: Jesse Wright

Tel:

International Plastic Modellers Society
Tyneside Branch
53 Killingworth Ave, Castle Pk
Backworth
Tyne & Wear

Tel: 091 268 9344

MAFAA
128 Chiltern Road
Bardock
Hertfordshire SG7 6LU

Contact: Paul Middleton

Manx Military Modelling Society
62 Port-E-Chee Avenue
Douglas
Isle of Man

Contact: David Sharpe

Tel: 0624 676084

Society formed to promote both large scale military modelling and historical based wargaming. Adult subscription £7.00, no age restrictions.

Miniature Armoured Fighting Vehicle Soc
3 Sussex House
Raymond Rd
London SW19 4AH

Tel: 071 879 1095

Miniature Armoured Fighting Vehicles Association
15 Berwick Avenue
Heaton Mersey
Stockport
Cheshire SK4 3AA

Contact: GEG Williams

Tel: 061 432 7574

Exists to promote interest in AFV's and their associated equipment. Information is disseminated through Tankette, a bi-monthly magazine containing articles, photos and plans of interest to both historian and model maker. Contact for details of local branches.

North Surrey Military Group
5 Flimwell Close
Bromley
Kent BR1 4NB

Tel: 081 698 0890

Plymouth Model Soldier Society
102 Warleigh Avenue
Keyham
Plymouth
Devon PL2 1NP

Contact: Harry Miller

Tel: 0752 556811

SE Essex IPMS
3 Curtis Way
Rayleigh
Essex SS6 8BU

Tel: 0268 777308

Shepway Military Modelling Soc
c/o The Trumpet Banner
88a Sandgate High Street
Folkestone
Kent CT20 3BY

Sutton Coldfield Model Makers
60 Severn Drive
Burntwood
West Midlands WS7 9JF

Contact: E Jones

Tel: 05436 74352

Swindon Military Modellers
20 Bryanston Way
Nythe
Swindon
Wiltshire SN3 3PG

Contact: Michael Copland

Tel: 0793 642020

Modelling group meets fortnightly (Sun). All standards and age groups.

The Leicester Modellers
Thurmaston Working Men's Club
Old Melton Road
Thurmaston
Leicester

Tel: 0533 671057

The North East Modellers
6 Jude Place
Peterlee
Co Durham SR8 5JW

Contact: Len Swaisland

Tel: 091 5867139

Universal Modelling Society
Midland Adult School Union Ctr
Gaywood Croft, Cregoe Street
Lee Bank
West Midlands B15 2ED

Contact: Den Karsey

Tel: 021 705 4085

Over fifty members whose interests
cover a wide range of modelling
including military figures, ships, planes,
armoured fighting vehicles, space and
science fiction. Participates in major
shows and holds own annual show.
Meetings weekly, Mon

7.30pm–10.00pm.

Waveney Modelling Group
10 Green Drive
Lowestoft
Suffolk

Contact: Dave Jervis

**West of Scotland Military
Modelling Club**
39 Riverside Park
Linnpark Avenue
Glasgow G44 3PG

Contact: The Secretary

Tel: 041 633 2344

Model Painters

Ace Models
Fountain Arcade
Dudley DY1 1PG

Tel: 0384 257045

Art Militaire
6 Gypsy Lane
Oulton
Leeds LS26 8SA

Contact: A. Buttery

Baldwin, Charles
4 Cooper Row
Southgate
Crawley
West Sussex RH10 6DJ

Tel: 0293 521288

Specialises in Napoleonic military figures larger than 54mm. Price list and photos available on receipt of a large stamped, addressed envelope or 4 international reply coupons.

Betteridge, Cptn. Brian
55 Prestop Drive
Westfields
Ashby Dela Zouch
Leicestershire LE6 4NA

Tel: 0530 560164

B.J. Harris Professional Figure Painting
123 Coverside Road
Great Glen
Leicester LE8 0EB

Tel: 0533 592004

Member of The Guild of Master Craftsmen. World wide mail order – all types of figures painted and assembled. Sizes from 15mm to 120mm, military and non–military subjects. Send 7 x 24p stamps for full colour brochure.

GM Painting Services
Church Lodge
Hanly Swan
Worcester WR8 0DE

HQ Painting Services
114 Windmill Hill Lane
Derby DE3 3BP

Contact: Paul Spencer

Tel: 0332 298519

Specialists in the hand painting of wargames figures and accessories. All scales from 5mm–120mm. Send s.a.e. for full details.

Mr G. Otty
50 Willbye Avenue
Diss
Norfolk IP22 3NW

Paint Box
April Cottage
49 Stonely
Huntingdon
Cambs PE18 0EP

Richard Newth–Gibbs Painting Services
59 Victor Close
Hornchurch
Essex RM12 4XH

Tel: 04024 48785

15mm to any scale, single figures, groups, dioramas, artillery pieces, mounted gun teams, British and Indian army specialist. Factual military work only. Callers by appointment.

Stuart West Figures
74 Rotherham Road
Holbrooks
Coventry
West Midlands CV6 4FE

Contact: Stuart West

Tel: 0203 666376

Specialises in white metal and resin figures from 54mm, 90mm and 120mm. Also suppliers of original hand painted toy soldiers in boxed sets. Full painting service is also available in all scales. Mail order service only and can supply to the trade.

The Iron Duke
Edgehill Cottage
Ropeyard
Wotton Bassett
Wilts SN4 7BW

Contact: Ian Barstow

Tel: 0793 850805

Professional wargames figure painter and dealer in second hand painted figures and armies. All scales. Guaranteed no sub–contracting. All major credit cards.

The Painted Soldier
138 Friern Road
East Dulwich
London SE22 0AY

Contact: Bill Brewer

Tel: 081 693 2449

Painting service for wargamers and collectors established for 25 years. Work on show at studio and has yearly trade stand at 'Salute', Chelsea and Kensington Town Hall.

Warpaint Figure Painting
20 Swaledale Crescent
Barnwell
Houghton–le–Spring
Tyne and Wear DH4 7NT

Tel: 091 385 7070

Toy Soldier Makers & Suppliers

Arkova
29 Taw View
Fremington
Barnstaple
Devon EX31 2NJ

Contact: Allan R. Over

Bastion Models
36 St. Mary's Road
Liss
Hampshire GU33 7AH

Contact: Andrew Rose

Britains Petite Ltd.
Chelsea Street
New Basford
Nottingham NG7 7HR

Bulldog Enterprises
64 Vivian Road
Sketty
Swansea
West Glamorgan SA2 0UL

Contact: Betty Jones

Tel: 0792 205972

Manufacturers of toy soldiers, mainly British army types of the late 19th/early 20th century in foreign and home service dress. Hand-painted in traditional style. Range in production since the early 1970's.

Campaign Miniatures
5 Barrowgate Road
Chiswick
London W4 4QX

Contact: Peter Johnstone

Charles Hall Productions
Paisley Terrace
Edinburgh EH8 7JW

Contact: Charles Hall

Connoisseur Figures
20a Coastal Road
Burniston
Scarborough
North Yorks YO13 0HR

Contact: Chris Gilder

Tel: 0723 870741
Fax: 0723 870741

Specialists in 25mm figures. Full mail order catalogue available with all their ranges, Napoleonic, Colonial, Pony Wars, American Civil War, Renaissance etc. 20% discount on all figures bought from their shop.

Derek Cross (AQM) Ltd.
The Old Cottage
Gilmorton
Lutterworth
Leics LE17 5PN

Contact: Derek Cross

Tel: 0455 552653
Fax: 0455 557787

Manufacturers of All The Queen's Men toy soldiers and collectors 80mm/90mm series. Colour catalogue (toy soldier) £12.00, Collectors series £6.00 (b/white). Viewing by appointment only, Mon-Sat. World wide mail order.

Dorset (Metal Model) Soldiers Ltd.
Latimer House
Castle Street
Mere
Wilts BA12 6JE

Contact: Giles Brown

Tel: 0747 860954
Fax: 0747 861210

Manufacturers of old 'toy style' lead soldiers/civilians and plastic figures. Also suppliers of various ranges. Send s.a.e. or 2 IRC's for further details.

Drill Square Toy Soldiers
8 Orchard Close
Towcester
Northamptonshire NN12 7BP

Contact: Dave Sparrow

Eagle Miniatures
Wild Acre
Minchinhampton
Glos GL6 9AJ

Contact: David Atkins

Tel: 0453 835782

Design, manufacture and distribute 15mm, 25mm and 54mm figures from the Seven Years, Napoleonic and American Civil War. A 'design and cast' service is available. Call by appointment. Occasionally hosts megagames.

Ensign Historical Miniatures
8 Hollins Meadow
Walsden
Todmorden
Lancs OL14 6PZ

Contact: Paul Wood

Tel: 0706 818203
Fax: 0706 817204

Manufacturers of white metal 1/32nd, 54mm scale traditional toy soldiers. Ranges include: English Civil War, British Colonial, Indian Army and Austro-Hungarians. All figures available boxed and painted or as unpainted castings. Issuers of exclusive limited edition sets. Send large s.a.e. for latest listings. Worldwide mail order.

Fact & Fantasy Models
44 Bretby Road
Newhall
Burton-on-Trent DE11 0LJ

Tel: 0283 550421

Forbes & Thomson
Burgate Antiques Centre
10c Burgate
Canterbury
Kent

Contact: Rowena Forbes/Thelma Thomson

Tel: 081 688 6698

Specialist dealers in old toy soldiers by Britains, Johillco etc. and related lead and tinplate toys. Model soldiers & kits by Rose Models and Chota Sahib. Painted military miniature figures. Mail order and office address, P.O. Box 375, South Croydon, CR2 6ZG. Open Mon-Sat 10.00am-5.00pm.

GPM Models
Twiga Lodge
Victoria Avenue
Kirkby-le-Soken
Essex CO13 0DJ

Tel: 0255 673013

Gerry Ford Designs
43 Queens Road
Farnborough
Hampshire GU14 6JP

Glebe Miniatures
Retreat House
Dorchester Road
Broadwey, Weymouth
Dorset DT3 5LN

Contact: Peter Turner

Tel: 0305 815300

Part of Monmouth Metal Toys producing castings and painted toy soldiers in the style of early Britains, their range is mainly late 19th and early 20th century British, European and other figures. Particular lines are the Indian Army, Russian, Balkan, Boer War, full dress and service. Horse, Foot and Artillery.

Good Soldiers
246 Broadwater Crescent
Stevenage
Herts SG2 8HL

Contact: Alan Goodwin

Tel: 0438 354362 (pm)

Producers of 'toy style' soldiers and figures. These are available painted and unpainted. Trade enquiries welcomed.

Granfield, Laurie
20 Whittan Close
Rhoose CF6 9FW
Wales

Contact: Laurie Granfield

Great Britain and the Empire
The Cedars
97 High Street
Coningsby
Lincs LN4 4RF

Contact: Andrew Humphries

Tel: 0526 42012

Over 600 types of hand painted, traditional toy soldiers. Covers different Regiments of the British army from 1870's – 1914. Send for catalogue. Figures purchased direct by mail order.

HM of Great Britain Ltd.
Unit 8
22 Leyburn Road
Sheffield S8 0XA

Contact: Peter Kingland

Lancashire Games (Mail Order)
20 Platting Road
Lydgate
Oldham
Lancs OL4 4DL

Contact: Allan Lumley

Tel: 0497 872212

Offers a range of miniatures from Renaissance to Colonial in 15mm, main ranges are horse and musket periods (Seven Years War to American Civil War). Painting service available on own range of miniatures and most other popular manufacturers. Send s.a.e. for full lists.

London Toy Soldiers
47 Tottenham Lane
Hornsey
London N8 9BD

Contact: Chris Fruin

Tel: 081 340 2184
Fax: 081 340 0457

Specialise in collectable old toy soldiers in lead, plastic and modern zinc alloy or lead production. Also produce own range of lead figures and vehicles. Open Tues–Sat, 10.30am–4.30pm. Mail order, send £1.00 for catalogue.

MKL Models
PO Box 32
Wokingham
Berks RG11 4ZX

Contact: Lynn Kenwood

Tel: 0734 733690

Mainly Military
61 Fore Street
Ilfracombe
Devon EX34 9DJ

Militia Models
Rosedean
Gorsty Knoll
Coleford
Gloucestershire GL16 7LR

Contact: Esme Walker

Museum of the Royal Scots Dragoon Guard
The Castle
Edinburgh EH1 2YT

Contact: Lt Col J.L. Wilson Smith

Tel: 031 336 1761 X4265

Regimental museum telling history of The Royal Scots. Museum shop selling regimental souvenirs, badges, buttons etc. Send s.a.e. for list. Open Mon–Sat 9.30am–4.00pm, Sun 11.30am–4.00pm, closed weekends October to March.

M.J. Mode
15 Station Road
Carcroft
Nr Doncaster
S. Yorks DN6 8DB

Contact: Mr S Murray

Navwar
11 Electric Parade
Seven Kings Road
Ilford
Essex IG3 8BY

Contact: William McKenzie

Tel: 081 590 6731
Fax: 081 590 6731

Manufacturers of 1/1200th and 1/3000th ships, Naismith Design, Roundway Miniatures and Heroics and Ros Figures, Publishers. Complete selection of Osprey, wargame rules, paint and action zoo. Mail order specialists. Trade enquiries welcome. Open Mon–Sat (except Thurs), 9.00am–5.30pm.

Opperman, George
Flat 12
110/112 Bath Road
Cheltenham
Glos GL35 7JX

Contact: George Opperman

Private collector with large collection to sell. 50,000 lead soldiers, military books and magazines, post and cigarette cards. Send s.a.e. and 3 x 1st class stamps for lists. Mail order only.

P & B Castings
13 Wharf Street
Goldaming
Surrey GU7 1NN

Piper Craft
4 Hillside Cottages
Glenboig
Lanarkshire ML5 2QY

Contact: Thomas Moles

Tel: 0236 873801
Fax: 0236 873044

Manufacturer of white metal military and non–military figures designed to a general scale of 75mm 93". Suppliers to museums, places of historic interest, shops and collectors. Established 1985. Send s.a.e. or 2 x IRC's for a complete illustrated list.

Pride of Europe
Shamrock Villa
Southernhay, Clifton Wood
Bristol BS8 4TL

Contact: Mr RJ Dew

Prince August U.K. Ltd.
Small Dole
Henfield
Sussex BN5 9XH

Quality Model Soldiers
Hippins Farm
Blackshawshead
Hebden Bridge
West Yorkshire HX7 7JG

Contact: G.M. Haley

RAE Models
Unit 2 Service Road
off Corrie Road
Addlestone
Surrey KT15 2LP

Raventhorpe Miniatures
2 Bygot Lane
Cherry Burton
Beverley
Humberside HU17 7RN

Contact: Anthony Chadburn

Tel: 0964 551027

20mm WWI and WWII specialist mail order. Send s.a.e. and 2 x 1st class stamps for catalogue.

Replica Models
40 Durbar Avenue
Foleshill
Coventry CV6 5LU

Tel: 0203 684338

SAC Ltd.
Flinton Street
Hull HU3 4NB

Sarum Soldiers Ltd.
2a Upper Tooting Park
London SW17 7SW

Contact: Patrick Willis

Tel: 081 767 1525

Manufacturer and retailer of Sarum Studio Figurines and Sarum Traditional Soliders in 54mm scale. Studio figurines include the 'History of the Regiments' series, designed by Andrew C. Stadden. Toy soldiers include 'Armies of the Great Powers, 1870-1914', and modern British army in ceremonial uniforms.

Simply Soldiers
A15 The Cowdray Centre
Colchester
Essex CO1 1BH

Soldier's Soldiers
Old Telephone Exchange
Eckington
Pershore
Worcs WR10 3AP

Contact: John Tunstill
Fax: 0386 750 133

Mail order only. New toy soldiers. Over three hundred 54mm model/toy figures. Mainly British Army 1880-1914 but also combating WWII nations and British Falklands figures. Lists available of boxes, sets and single figures – painted and unpainted. Send s.a.e. and 3 x 1st class stamps.

Stuart West Figures
74 Rotherham Road
Holbrooks
Coventry
West Midlands CV6 4FE

Contact: Stuart West

Tel: 0203 666376

Specialises in white metal and resin figures from 54mm, 90mm and 120mm. Also suppliers of original hand painted toy soldiers in boxed sets. Full painting service is also available in all scales. Mail order service only and can supply to the trade.

T & M Models
44 Watersmeet
Northampton NN1 5SG

The Armoury of St. James
17 Piccadilly Arcade
Piccadilly
London SW1Y 6NH

Contact: Mark St. Clair

The Army Supply Company
6 Old Bank
Ripponden
Halifax
West Yorkshire HX6 4DG

Contact: Michael Carter

The Mad Colonel
37 Mildmay Park
Islington
London N1 4NA

Contact: Marc St. Clare

Tel: 071 354 3259

Supplier of military items from original sources. Commissions undertaken. Extensive search capability. Large network provides toy soldiers, ship and aircraft models, new and antique dinky toys. All military collectables and curios bought and sold. Write or phone with requirements.

The Parade Ground
6 Seventh Avenue
Bridlington
Nrth Humberside YO15 2LQ

Tel: 0262 673724

The Red Box Toy Soldier Co.
Manor Field Galleries
Manor Field House
Aston-Cum-Aughton
Sheffield S31 0XJ

Contact: Dennis Johnson

The Thin Red Line
8 Canoustie Drive
Fornham St. Martin
Bury St Edmunds
Suffolk IP28 6UU

Tel: 0284 705423

Toyway
PO Box 55, Unit 20
Jubilee Trade Cntr, Jubilee Rd
Letchworth
Herts SG6 1SG

Contact: Richard Morriss

Tel: 0462 672509
Fax: 0462 672132

Tradition
2 Shepherd Street
Mayfair
London W1Y 7LN

Tel: 071 493 7452
Fax: 071 355 1224

One of the longest established manufacturers and retailers in the model soldier field, its London showrooms a Mecca for many collectors. Painted and unpainted figures are available in all popular scales 54mm, 90mm and 110mm, with armies from the ancient world to the present day. Troops of the Napoleonic wars and the British army through the ages are a speciality. Also manufacturer of over 200 different toy soldier boxed sets with new releases every month, which are also available unpainted. In the smaller scales 25mm & 30mm figures are made, including the famous 'Willie' range for dioramas. Open Mon–Fri 9.00am–5.30pm, Sat 9.30am–3.00pm. Catalogues are available for all sizes.

Tradition at 10 Whitehorse Street, W.1. (071 491 7077) specialises in pre-1914 militaria including uniforms, prints and paintings. Open by appointment.

Trafalgar Models
122 Lazy Hill Road
Aldridge
Walsall
West Midlands WS9 8RR

Under Two Flags
4 Saint Christopher's Place
London W1M 5HB

Contact: Jack Coutts

Tel: 071 935 6934

Stockist of toy soldiers, model kits, military books, painted figures & dioramas. Open Mon-Sat, 10.00am-5.00pm.

VR Sime Supply
24 Tollhouse Road
Crossgate Moor
Durham
Co. Durham DH1 4HV

Contact: David & Mary Reay

Tel: 0911 3842724

Firm specialising in mail order and supplying to overseas customers. Write with requirements.

V.C. Miniatures
16 Dunraven Street
Aberkenfig
Nr Bidgend
Mid Glam CF32 9AS

Contact: Lyn Thorne

Tel: 0656 725006

Established 1987, manufacturer of hand painted 54mm toy soldiers, sculpted by Lyn Thorne and specialising in the Victorian period. In addition to sets of traditional toy soldiers, military and civilian vignette's and individual figures are also produced. Recently acquired are Burlington Models range of racehorses, jockey's and showjumping figures. The full range of Burlington horses are available. The range will be expanded in the near future. European distributor of Victorian miniatures The Zulu Line, a range consisting of over 240 different Zulu's in action poses, which are available as pointed sets or in kit form. Available from many dealers or direct by mail order.

Whittlesey Miniatures
6 St Mary's Street
Whittlesey
Nr. Petersborough
Cambs

Museums

101 Field Reg. Royal Artillery
T.A. Centre, Knightsbridge
Gosforth
Newcastle

17th/21st Lancers Reg. Museum
Belvoir Castle
Nr Grantham
Nr. Grantham
Lincolnshire NG33 7TJ

Tel: 0476 67413 X252

1st The Queen's Dragoon Guards Reg. Mus.
Clive House
College Hill
Shrewsbury SY1 1LZ

Tel: 0743 54811

21st Special Air Service Regimental Mus.
B Block, Duke of York's HQ
King's Rd
London SW3 4SE

Tel: 071 930 4466

4th (V) Royal Green Jackets
56 Davies Street
London
London W1

Tel: 071 748 3677

94 Signal Squadron Museum
TAVR Centre
Bolton Road
Windsor
Berkshire SL4 3JG

Tel: 07535 60600

Abingdon Museum
County Hall
Market Place
Abingdon
Oxon

Tel: 0235 23703

Airborne Forces Museum
Browning Barracks
Aldershot
Hants GU11 2BU

Contact: Diana Andrews

Tel: 0252 349619
Fax: 0252 349203

Open daily 10.00am–4.30pm, closed Mondays. Admission £1.25 adults, 60p children, OAP's & ex servicemen. Gift shop. Suitable for disabled. Free parking. Shop list available by post.

Aldershot Army Catering Corps
R.H.Q.,
St. Omer Barracks
Aldershot
Hants GU11 2BW

Tel: 0252 24431 X2616

Aldershot Army Physical Training Corps
Corps Depot
Queen's Avenue
Aldershot
Hants GU11 2LB

Tel: 0252 24431 X2131

Aldershot Gurkha Museum
Queen Elizabeth Barracks
Church Crookham
Aldershot
Hants GU13 0RJ

Tel: 0252 613541

Aldershot Military Museum
Queen's Avenue
Aldershot
Hants GU11 2LG

Contact: The Curator

Tel: 0252 314598

Looks behind the scenes at daily life of both soldier and civilian over 140 years as Aldershot and Farnborough grew up around the Camp. Galleries of WWII Canadian Army in Aldershot and Europe, local history, Yeomanry and Volunteers, early aviation at Farnborough. Open daily 10.00am–4.30pm. Shop.

Ayrshire Yeomanry Museum
Rozelle House
Monument Road
Alloway by Ayr KA7 4NQ

Tel: 0465 3119

Battle & Dis. Historical Mus.
Langton House
Abbey Green
Battle
Sussex TN33 0AQ

Blackburn Museum & Art Gallery
Museum Street
Blackburn
Lancs BB1 7AJ

Tel: 0254 667130

Exhibits relating to the East Lancashire Regiment.

Bolling Hall Museum
Bowling Hall Road
Bradford
West Yorkshire

Tel: 0274 723057

British in India Museum
Sun Street
Colne
Lancashire BB8 0JJ

Tel: 0282 63129

Buckland Abbey

Near Yelverton

Devon

Tel: 0822 853607

Cambridgeshire Regiment
Ely Museum
28c High Street
Ely
Cambridgeshire

Contact: J.R. Stubbings

Tel: 0353 666655

Limited display of uniforms and equipment from The Cambridgeshire Regiment including the unique "Singapore Drums". Open Tues–Sat 10.30am–1.00pm, 2.15pm–5.00pm. Adults 80p, 6–16yrs 40p. For further information write to J.R. Stubbings, Hon. Sec. 25 The Vineyards, Ely, Cambs, CB7 4QC.

Cannon Hall Mus. & Art Gallery
Cannon Hall
Cawthorne
Barnsley
South Yorkshire S75 4AT

Tel: 0226 790270

Carmarthen Museum
Abergwili
Carmarthen
Dyfed

Tel: 0267 231691

Castle Museum
Tower Street
York YO1 1RY

Tel: 0904 53611

Houses exhibits relating to The 4th/7th Royal Dragoon Guards and The Prince of Wales's own Regiment of Yorkshire.

Cheshire Military Museum
The Castle
Chester CH1 2DN

Tel: 0244 27617

Chesterholm Museum
Vindolanda
Bardon Mill
Hexham
Northumberland

Tel: Bardon Mill 277

Chomondeley Collection of Toy Soldiers
Houghton Hall
Kings Lynn
Norfolk

City Museum
Market Square
Lancaster
Lancashire LA1 1HT

Tel: 0524 64637

City Museum
Municipal Buildings
Leeds
Yorkshire LS1 3AA

Tel: 0532 462632

City Museum & Art Gallery
Bethesda Street
Hanley
Stoke-on-Trent ST1 3DW

Tel: 0782 202173

Clayton Memorial Mus./Chester Roman Fort
Chollerford
Hexham
Northumberland

Tel: Humshaugh 379

Cobbaton Combat Collection
Chittlehampton
Umberleigh
North Devon EX37 9SO

Contact: Preston Issac

Tel: 0769 540740
Fax: 0769 540740

Private collection of over 50 vehicles. Tanks, carriers, A.F.V's, trucks, gun tractors, artillery. Radios, weapons and thousands of smaller items from WWII British, Canadian and Warsaw Pact. Also seperate 'Home Front' building shop selling militaria, deactivated weapons and models. Open April–Oct 7 days, winter Mon–Fri. Adults £2.50, children £1.25.

Colchester & Essex Museum
The Hollytrees
The High Street
Colchester
Essex

Tel: 0206 712481/2

Combined Operations Museum
Cherry Park
Inverary Castle
Inverary
Argyle PA32 8XE

Contact: Director

Tel: 0499 2203
Fax: 0499 2421

C.T.C. World War II exhibits including newspapers, battle plans and scale models of landing craft and ships. Open May–Sept. Admission adults 90p, children/senior citizens 60p.

Cornwall Aircraft Park
Clodgey Lane
Helston
Helston
Cornwall TR13 0GA

Tel: 0326 573404

Corps of Royal Military Police
Roussillon Barracks
Chichester
Sussex PO19 4BN

County & Regimental Museum
Stanley Street
Preston
Lancashire PR1 4YP

Contact: Dr Stephen Bull

Tel: 0772 264075

The museum covers several local regiments including The 14/20th Hussars, Duke of Lancaster's Own Yeomanry and Queens Lancashire Regiments, also Militia and Volunteers of the County. There are frequent special exhibitions, many with a military theme. Open Mon–Sat (except Thurs), 10.00am–5.00pm.

Doncaster Museum & Art Gallery
Chequer Road
Doncaster
Sth Yorkshire DN1 2AE

Tel: 0302 734287

Dorset Military Museum
The Keep
Dorchester
Dorset DT1 1RN

Contact: The Curator

Tel: 0305 264066

Old photographs, paintings, uniforms, weapons, medals and other militaria that belonged to the County's units past and present. The units go back as far as 1702 and include The Dorset Regiment, Queen's Own Dorset Yeomanry, Rifle Volunteers, Militia, Home Guard and the present day Devonshire and Dorset Regiment.

Duke of Cornwall's Light Infantry Museum
The Keep
Bodmin
Cornwall PL31 1EG

Tel: 0208 2810

Duke of Wellington's Regimental Museum
Bankfield Museum
Akroyd Park
Halifax
West Yorkshire HX3 6HG

Contact: The Curator

Tel: 0422 352334

Depicts the history of The 33rd and 76th Regiments, together with associated Volunteer and Territorial Units from 1702 to present day. Includes a display devoted to the 'Iron Duke'. Open Tues–Sat 10.00am–5.00pm, Sun 2.00pm–5.00pm.

Durham Light Infantry Museum
Aykley Heads
Durham
Durham DH1 5TU

Contact: The Curator

Tel: 091 384 2214

Houses exhibition on The Durham Light Infantry from 1758–1968 including uniforms, medals, weapons, photographs and Regimental treasures. Open Tues–Sat 10.00am–5.00pm, Sun 2.00pm–5.00pm. Shop and coffee bar. Access for disabled.

Duxford Imperial War Museum
Duxford Airfield
Duxford
Cambridge CB2 4QR

Tel: 0223 833963

D-Day Museum & Overlord Embroidery
Clarence Esplanade
Southsea PO5 3NT

D.H. Mosquito Aircraft Museum
Salisbury Hall
London Colney
Nr St Albans
Hertfordshire

Edgehill Battle Museum
The Estate Yard
Farnborough Hall, Farnborough
Banbury
Oxfordshire OX17 1DU

Contact: Curator

Tel: 0926 332213
Fax: 0926 336795

Commemorating the first major battle of The English Civil War. Large diorama depicts the battle plus life size models, flags, weapons, uniforms and music. Bookshop & refreshments. Battlefield tours for groups by arrangement. Open April to September, Wed & Sat, 2.00pm–6.00pm. Admission £1.00, 50p concessions.

Essex Regiment Museum
Oaklands Park
Moulsham Street
Chelmsford
Essex CM2 9AQ

Contact: Ian Hook

Tel: 0245 260614

The museum for The Essex Regiment and its forebears, The 44th and 56th Foot. The Regiment is now part of The Royal Anglican Regiment. Permanent displays of weapons, uniforms, medals, silver and relics. Open Mon–Sat 10.00am–5.00pm, Sundays 2.00pm–5.00pm.

Fleet Air Arm Museum
R.N.A. Station
Yeovilton
Somerset BA22 8HT

Contact: Jane Hodgkins   ·

Tel: 0935 840565
Fax: 0935 840181

Over fifty historic aircraft on display including Concorde 002. Five major new exhibitions recently opened including The Harrier Jump Jet Story and The Underwater Experience. Other exhibitions on display are WWI, WWII, The Wrens & The Falklands. Flight simulator, airfield viewing galleries and childrens aviation adventure playground.

Fort Cumberland/Portsmouth Militaria Soc
c/o 49 Lichfield Road
Portsmouth
Hants PO3 6DD

Contact: David Quinton

Tel: 0705 668981

HQ & museum adjacent to Round Tower, Broad Street, Old Portsmouth. Local and military history, postcards & books. Re-enactment group Fort Cumberland Guard Royal Marines 1835–40 period musket & cannon displays. Drum corps have been featured on TV frequently. Free. Mon 7.30pm–9.30pm, Sunday 2.00pm–5.00pm.

Fusiliers Volunteer & Territorial Museum
213 Balham High Road
London SW17 7BQ

Tel: 081 672 1168

German Underground Hospital
St. Lawrence
Jersey
Channel Islands

Tel: 0534 63442

Glasgow Art Gallery & Museum
Kelvingrove
Glasgow
Strathclyde G3 8AG

Contact: Robert Woosnam-Savage

Tel: 041 357 3929
Fax: 041 357 4537

Collection of European arms and armour, 1000 A.D. – early 20th Century. Includes the 'Avant' armour, c.1440–5, the earliest and most complete armour in the British Isles (part of the R.L. Scott Collection); Whitelaw Collection of Scottish arms; Martin Collection of firearms; material of Scottish W. Coast Volunteer Units (18th & 19th Century). Closed Dec 25, Jan 1.

Gordon Highlanders Reg. Museum
R.H.Q.
Viewfield Road
Aberdeen

Tel: 0224 318174

Grange Cavern Military Museum
Grange lane
Holway
Holywell
Clwyd

Tel: 0352 713455

Guards Museum
Wellington Barracks
Birdcage Walk
London SW1A 2AX

Tel: 071 930 4466

HMS Belfast
Morgan's Lane
Tooley Street
London SE1 2JH

Contact: Sarah Hogben

Tel: 071 407 6434
Fax: 071 403 0719

Europe's largest preserved WWII warship. Seven decks to visit including the bridge, gun turrets, mess decks, engine rooms etc.. Open Mon–Sun, from 10.00am.

Hereford Reg. & Light Infantry Museum
T.A. Centre
Harold Street
Hereford

Tel: 0432 272914

Hertford Museum
18 Bull Plain
Hertford SG14 1DJ

Tel: 0992 272914

Hever Castle
Nr. Tonbridge
Kent

Tel: 0732 865224

Hitchin Museum
Paynes Park
Hitchin
Hertfordshire SG5 1EQ

Tel: 0462 34476

Hertfordshire Yeomanry and Artillery historical museum.

Honourable Artillery Company
Armoury House
City Road
London EC1Y 2BQ

Household Cavalry Museum
Combermere Barracks
St. Leonards Road
Windsor
Berkshire SL4 3DN

Contact: Major A.W. Kersting

Tel: 07535 868222 X5203

Collection contains uniforms, weapons, horse furniture, standards and curios of The Regiment of the Household Cavalry. Over 300 years of the history of The Sovereigns Mounted Bodyguard. Open Mon–Fri, 9.30am–12.30pm 2.00pm–4.30pm. Free admission.

Hull City Museums
Wilberforce House
High Street
Hull

Tel: 0482 222737

Huntly House Museum
142 Canongate
Edinburgh EH8 8DD

Contact: The Curator

Tel: 031 225 2424 X6689
Fax: 031 557 3346

Edinburgh's main museum of local history. Displays include collections relating to the life of Field–Marshal Earl Haig (1861–1928), with a reconstruction of his WWI HQ. Open Mon–Sat 10.00am–5.00pm (Oct–May), 10.00am–6.00pm (June–Sept), Sunday 2.00pm–5.00pm (during Edingburgh Festival). Admission free.

Imperial War Museum
Lambeth Road
London SE1 6HZ

Contact: Linda Hart

Tel: 071 416 5000
Fax: 071 416 5374

A unique institution telling the story of 20th century warfare. It contains exhibitions on the two World Wars, a 'large exhibits' hall, art galleries, a cafe and a shop. Open Mon–Sun 10.00am–6.00pm. Admission adults £3.30, concessions £1.65. Tube Lambeth North, Elephant and Castle. British Rail – Waterloo, Elephant and Castle.

Inns of Court & City Yeomanry Museum
10 Stone Buildings
Lincoln's Inn
London WC2A 3TG

Tel: 071 405 8112

Intelligence Corps Museum
Templer Barracks
Ashford
Kent TN23 3HH

Tel: 0252 25251 X208

John G. Joicey Museum
City Road
Newcastle

Tel: 091 232 4562

Museum dedicated to The 15th and 19th King's Royal Hussars and Northumberland Hussars.

King's Own Scottish Borderers Regimental Musem
The Barracks
Berwick–U–Tweed
Northumberland TD15 1DG

Tel: 0289 307426

Langford Lodge
Gortnagallon Road
Crumlin
County Antrim BT29 4QR

Tel: 0232 650451

London Irish Rifles Regimental Museum
Duke of York's H.Q.
Kings Road
London SW1

London Scottish Reg. Museum
95 Horseferry Road
London SW1P 2DX

Tel: 071 630 1639

London War Museum
1–5 Crucifix Lane
London Bridge
London SE1

Lunt Roman Fort
Coventry Road
Baginton
Nr Coventry

Tel: 0203 25555 X2315

Luton Museum
Wardown Park
Luton
Bedfordshire LU2 7HA

Tel: 0582 36941

Museum of the Bedfordshire and Hertfordshire Regiments.

Maidstone Museum
St. Faith's Road
Maidstone
Kent ME14 1LH

Tel: 0622 54497

The Queen's Own Royal West Kent Regimental Museum.

Manchester Regiment Collection
The King's Regiment,
T.A. Centre, Ardwick Green,
Manchester M12 6HD

Tel: 061 434 1211

Mary Rose Ship Hall & Exhibition
HM Naval Base
Portsmouth

Tel: 0705 750521

Middlesex Regimental Museum
Bruce Castle
Lordship Lane
London N17 8NU

Tel: 081 808 8772

Middlesex & Uxbridge Yeomanry Signals Historical Trust
T.A.Centre, Elmgrove Road
Harrow
Middx HA1 2QA

Tel: 0992 57018

Midland Air Museum
Coventry Airport
Baginton
Warwickshire CV8 3AZ

Tel: 0203 301033

Military Vehicle Museum
Exhibition Park Pavillion
Newcastle NE2 4PZ

Tel: 091 281 7222

Museum of Army Flying
Army Air Corps Centre
Middle Wallop
Hampshire SO20 8DY

Tel: 0264 62121

Museum of Army Transport
Flemingate
Beverley
East Yorkshire HU17 0NG

Contact: Leonie Jordan

Tel: 0482 866549

Exhibits over 100 years of army transport. Includes last of the line 'The Blackburn Beverley Aircraft'. Restoration workshop, archives library with public reading room, shop with specialist stock and mail order. Free.

Museum of Artillery
The Rotunda
Woolwich
London SE18 4JJ

Tel: 081 854 2242

Museum of Duke of Edinburgh's Royal Reg.
The Wardrobe
58 The Close
Salisbury
Wiltshire SP1 2EX

Tel: 0722 336222

Museum of Gloucestershire Regiment
Custom House
Gloucester Docks
Gloucester GL1 2HE

Contact: The Curator

Tel: 0452 22682

A new museum in Gloucester's fascinating historic docks which was nominated 'Best Small Museum' of 1991. Displays include small scale dioramas, life size reconstructions, sound effects and Regimental memorabilia. Souvenir shop, mail order, admission charge. Open Tues–Sun, 10.00am–5.00pm.

Museum of Lincolnshire Life
Old Barracks
Burton Road
Lincoln
Lincolnshire LN1 3LY

Tel: 0522 528448

Features displays relating to The Lincolnshire Yeomanry, a WWI tank developed in Lincoln, and an entire gallery devoted to the 300 year history of The Lincolnshire Regiment. Open May–Sept everyday, 10.00am–5.30pm, Oct–April Mon–Sat 10.00am–5.30pm, Sun 2.00pm–5.30pm.

Museum of Nazi German Equipment & Occupation Relics
St Peter's Bunker
St Peter's
Jersey
Channel Islands

Tel: 0534 33825

Museum of Staffordshire Reg.
Whittington Barracks
Lichfield
Staffordshire WS14 9PY

Tel: 0543 433333

Museum of the Army Chaplains'
Bagshot Park
Surrey GU19 5PL

Tel: 0276 71717

Museum of the Irish Cavalry Regiments
Carrickfergus Castle
County Antrim

Tel: 096 03 51273

Museum of the King's Regiment
Liverpool Museum
William Brown Street
Liverpool L3 8EN

Tel: 051 207 0001

Museum of the Order of St.John
St. John's Gate
St. John's Lane
London EC1M 4DA

Contact: Amanda Devonshire

Tel: 071 253 6644
Fax: 071 490 8835

Sixteenth century gatehouse containing armour, silver, coins, medals and other objects of the Knights of St. John. Also uniforms, equipment, memorabilia and records of St. John Ambulance and wartime medical services. Mon–Fri 10.00am–5.00pm, Sat 10.00am–4.00pm. Tours of Gatehouse and Norman Crypt Tues, Fri & Sat 11.00am–2.30pm.

Museum of the Royal Highland Fusiliers
518 Sauchiehall Street
Glasgow G2 3LW

Tel: 041 332 0961

Museum of the Royal Scots Dragoon Guard
The Castle
Edinburgh EH1 2YT

Contact: Lt Col J.L. Wilson Smith

Tel: 031 336 1761 X4265

Regimental museum telling history of The Royal Scots. Museum shop selling regimental souvenirs, badges, buttons etc. Send s.a.e. for list. Open Mon–Sat 9.30am–4.00pm, Sun 11.30am–4.00pm, closed weekends October to March.

National Maritime Museum
Greenwich
London SE10 9NF

Tel: 081 858 4422

National Museum of Antiquities of Scotland
Queen Street
Edinburgh EH2 1JD

Tel: 031 556 8921

Newark Air Museum
The Airfield
Winthorpe
Newark
Nottinghamshire NG24 2NY

Contact: Howard Heeley

Tel: 0636 707170

Located on an original bomber dispersal with nearly half of the 40 aircraft displayed undercover. Wide range of aircraft types displayed alongside aero engines, uniforms, aircraft parts, memorabilia. Admission adults £2.50, children and senior citizens £1.50.

Newark Museum
Appleton Gate
Newark
Nottinghamshire NG24 1JY

Contact: M.J. Hall

Tel: 0636 702358

Collections relating to The 8th Batallion Sherwood Foresters. Uniforms of Gonville Bromhead – by appointment only.

Newhaven Fort
Fort Road
Newhaven
East Sussex BN9 9DL

Contact: Ian Everest

Tel: 0273 517622

A restored Victorian coastal fortress which features a military museum, gun emplacements, underground installations and spectacular coastal views. Open Easter–Oct, Wed–Sun 10.30am–6.00pm. Daily during the school summer holiday.

Norfolk & Suffolk Aviation Museum
Flixton
Bungay
Suffolk

Tel: 050 843 778

Oxfordshire Regimental Museum
T.A. Centre
Slade Park
Headington
Oxford OX3 7JL

Tel: 0865 778479

Regimental museum of The Oxfordshire and Buckinghamshire Light Infantry.

Passmore Edwards Museum
Romford Road
Stratford
London E15 4LZ

Tel: 081 519 4296

Portland Basin Industrial Heritage Cntr
1 Portland Place
Portland Street South
Ashton–Under–Lyne
Lancs OL6 7SY

Contact: Geoff Preece

Tel: 061 308 3374

A museum dedicated to the social and Regimental history of The Manchester Regiment. Open Mon–Sat, 10.00am–4.00pm. Admission free.

Preston Hall Museum
Yarm Road
Stockton
Cleveland

Tel: 0642 781184

Public Record Office
Chancery Lane
London WC2A 1LR

Contact: Director

Tel: 081 876 3444

Access to military records.

Quebec House
Quebec Square
Westerham
Kent TN16 1TD

Tel: 0959 62206

Queen Alexandra's Royal Nursing Museum
Royal Pavillion
Farnborough Road
Aldershot
Hants GU11 1PZ

Tel: 0252 24431 X4315

Queen Mary's Tower
The Castle
Carlisle
Cumbria CA3 8UR

Contact: The Curator

Tel: 0228 32774

Exhibits relating to The Border Regiment and King's Own Royal Border Regiment.

Queen Royal Lancers & Staffordshire Mus.
Kitchener House
Lammascote Road
Stafford ST16 3TA

Tel: 0785 45840

Queen's Own Highlanders Reg. Museum
Fort George
Ardersier
Inverness

Tel: 0463 224380

Exhibits from Seaforth, Camerons, Lovat Scouts. Publishers of Regimental history. Pipe music, piping history. Shop and mail order. Books, postcards, prints, tapes etc. Open April–Sept Mon–Fri 10.00am–6.00pm, Sun 2.00pm–6.00pm, October–March, Mon–Fri 10.00am–4.00pm.

Queen's Royal Surrey Regiment Museum
Clandon Park
West Clandon
Guildford
Surrey GU4 7RQ

Tel: 0483 223419

RAF St Athan Historic Aircraft Collection
RAF St Athan
Barry
Glamorgan CF6 9WA

Tel: 0446 798798

Reg Mus 9th/12th Royal Lancers
Derby Museum and Art Gallery
The Strand
Derby
Derbyshire DE1 1BS

Contact: Nick Forder

Tel: 0332 255581

Collection includes uniforms and equipment from The 9th/12th Lancers Regiment, The Derbyshire Infantry and The Derbyshire Cavalry. Also houses the Imperial German Collection. Enquiry and identification service available. Open Mon 11.00am–5.00pm, Tues–Sat 10.00am–5.00pm, Sun 2.00pm–5.00pm.

Regimental Museum The Royal Irish Fusiliers
Sovereign's House, The Mall
Armagh BT61 9AJ

Tel: 0861 522911

Regimental Museum The Royal Inniskillen Fusiliers
The Castle
Inniskillen
Co. Fermanagh

Tel: 0365 23142

Regimental Museum of Transport
HQ, The Training Group RCT
Buller Barracks
Aldershot
Hants GU11 2BX

Tel: 0252 24431 X3837

Regimental Museum of the Royal Welsh Fusiliers
Queen's Tower
Caernarfon Castle
Caernarfon

Reg. Museum Queens Own Hussars
Lord Leycester Hospital
High Street
Warwick

Tel: 0926 492755

Reg. Museum of the Lancashire Fusiliers
Wellington Barracks
Bury
Lancs

Tel: 061 764 2208

Reg. Museum, The Cameronians
Mote Hill
Off Muir Street
Hamilton
Lanarkshire

Tel: 0698 428688

Reme Museum
Isaac Newton Road
Arborfield
Nr Reading
Berks RG2 9LN

Tel: 0734 760421

Roman Army Museum
Carvoran
Greenhead
Via Carlisle

Tel: 069 72 485

Royal Air Force Museum
Grahame Park Way
Hendon
London NW9 5LL

Tel: 081 205 2266
Fax: 081 200 1751

National Museum of Aviation with nearly seventy aircraft. Also collections of fine art, arms and armanent, equipment, uniforms and insignia of The Royal Air Force, its predecessors and the airforces of other nations. There is also an extensive library.

Royal Armouries
H.M. Tower of London
London EC3 4AB

Tel: 071 480 6358

The Royal Armouries, HM Tower of London, is the national museum of arms and armour. The collection includes pieces from the Dark Ages to the present day including sporting armours of Henry VIII and Charles I, a hunting and sporting collection, an oriental armoury and an extensive British military 18th & 19th century collection. Admission with Tower ticket. Open Mar–Oct, Mon–Sat 9.30am–5.45.pm, Sun 2.00pm–5.30pm; Nov–Feb Mon–Sat 9.30am–4.30pm, closed Sun. Underground Circle and District to Tower Hill. Bus 15, 42, 78. Riverboat to Tower Pier. Shop, mail order for specialist books and videos, arms and armour replicas, catalogue and newsletter for products and adult education courses available.

Royal Army Dental Corps Museum
HQ & Central Group RADC
Evelyn Woods Road
Aldershot
Hants

Tel: 0252 24431 X2782

Royal Army Educational Museum
RAEC Centre
Wilton Park
Beaconsfield
Bucks HP9 2RP

Tel: 0494 6121

Royal Army Medical Corps Museum
Keogh Barracks
Ash Vale
Nr Aldershot
Hants GU12 5RQ

Royal Army Ordnance Corps Museum
R.A.O.C. Training Centre
Blackdown Barracks, Deepcut
Camberley
Surrey GU16 6RW

Tel: 0252 24431

Royal Army Pay Corps
Worthy Down
Winchester
Hampshire SO21 2RG

Tel: 0962 880880

Royal Army Veterinary Museum
RAVC Support Group
Gallwey Road
Aldershot
Hants

Tel: 0252 24431 X3527

Royal Artillery Reg. Museum
Old Royal Military Academy
Academy Road
London SE18 4DN

Tel: 081 854 2242

Royal Devon Yeomanry
40 Oakleigh Road
Barnstaple
Nrth Devon EX32 8JT

Contact: J A Woolcott

Royal Engineers Museum
Brompton Barracks
Chatham
Kent ME4 4UG

Contact: The Curator

Tel: 0634 844555 X2371

Exhibition conveying the life and work of Britain's soldier engineers from 1066–1945. Open Tues–Fri, 10.00am–5.00pm, Sundays 11.30am–5.00pm. Admission Adults £1.00, Child/Senior Citizen 50p. Shop and refreshments.

Royal Leicestershire Regimental Museum
The Newarke
Oxford Street
Leicester

Tel: 0533 554100

Museum of The 15th and 19th King's Royal Hussars and The Northumberland Hussars.

Royal Marines Museum
Southsea
Portsmouth
Hampshire PO4 9PX

Tel: 0705 819385/831679
Fax: 0705 838420

The history of the Marines since 1664 to the present day, incorporating medal, uniform and weapon collections. Library and archive research facilities available by appointment. Photographic library with copying service. Museum shop with mail order department. Open Mon–Sun, 10am–4.40pm.

Royal Military Academy
Sandurst Collection
RMAS Camberley
Surrey

Tel: 0276 63344 X489

Royal Military School of Music
Museum
Kneller Hall
Twickenham
Middlesex TW2 7DU

Tel: 081 898 5533

Royal Navy Museum
H.M. Naval Base
Portsmouth
Hampshire PO1 3LR

Tel: 0705 733060

Royal Navy Submarine Museum
Hascar Jetty Road
Gosport
Hampshire PO12 2AS

Contact: Graham Dobbin

Tel: 0705 510354
Fax: 0705 511349

Archive department can supply B/W prints of photographs, copies of drawings and plans. Giftshop stocks books, kits etc. Available by mail order. Open Nov–March 10.00am–3.30pm, April–Oct 10.00am–4.30pm. Adult admission £3.00.

Royal Northumberland Regimental Museum
Abbot's Tower
Alnwick Castle
Alnwick
Northumberland NE66 1NG

Tel: 0665 602152

The Fifth or Royal Northumberland Fusiliers Regimental Museum.

Royal Pioneer Corps Museum
Corps H.Q.
Simpson Barracks
Wootton
Northampton NN4 0HX

Contact: Corps Secretary

Tel: 0604 762742 X4705

Displays include items of military interest, uniforms, badges, weapons, medals of The Corps. South of Northampton on the B526. Open Mon–Fri 9.30am–12.00pm 2.00pm–4.00pm, Fri 2.00pm–3.00pm. Bank holidays and weekends by appointment. Wheelchair access but no toilets. Shop.

Royal Regiment of Wales Museum

The Barracks
Brecon
Powys LD3 7EB

Contact: Major R.P. Smith

Tel: 0874 623111 X2310
Fax: 0874 623111-2496

The Museum is divided into four rooms. The main room contains a wide variety of interesting artefacts, ranging from uniforms and equipment to letters, documents and paintings detailing the history of The Regiment from 1689 to its amalgamation with The Welch Regiment in 1969 and onwards to the present day as The Royal Regiment of Wales. The Zulu War room contains an interesting collection of relics from the battles of Isandhlwana and Rorke's Drift. The medal room houses well over 200 medals – also on display are replicas of 16 of the 24 VCs won by the Regiment. The Armoury contains a large number of weapons both British and foreign. An audio-visual facility runs for 19 minutes, describing the events in January 1879 when The 24th Regiment fought in the Zulu War and gained ten Victoria Crosses. The archives contain war diaries, army lists, photographs, maps and documents.

Royal Signals Museum

Blandford Camp
Blandford Forum
Dorset DT11 8RH

Contact: Dr Peter Thwaites

Tel: 0258 482263

Displays items relating to the history of army signalling since the Crimean War as well as the history of the Royal Corps of Signals. Admission free. Open Mon-Fri 10.00am-5.00pm, Sat/Sun only June-Sept, 10.00am-4.00pm.

Rutland County Museum

Catmos Street
Oakham
Rutland LE15 6HW

Tel: 0572 3654

R.A.F. Regiment Museum

RAF Regiment Depot
RAF Catterick
Nrth Yorkshire

Tel: 0748 811441 X202

Saffron Walden Museum

Museum Street
Saffron Walden
Essex CB10 1JL

Tel: 0799 22494

Science Museum

Exhibition Road
South Kensington
London SW7 2DD

Tel: 071 589 6371

Scottish United Service Museum

The Castle
Edinburgh EH1 2NG

Contact: Stephen Wood

Tel: 031 225 7534
Fax: 031 225 3848

Scotland's national museum of the Armed Services. Collections include a large and comprehensive range of all types of Scottish military antiquities and a large library and archive, available for use by appointment (tel. ext. 404). Open 9.30am-5.30pm. Entrance fee to Castle.

Sherwood Rangers

T.A. Centre
Carlton
Nottingham

Somerset Military Museum

County Museum
The Castle
Taunton
Somerset TA1 4AA

Tel: 0823 333434

South Lancashire Regiment Museum RHQ QLR

Peninsula Barracks
O'Leary Street
Warrington
Cheshire WA2 7BR

Contact: Lt Colonel EG Bostock

Tel: 0925 33563

Contains artefacts and records of The 40th & 82nd Regiment and Volunteer Services 1717-1881. The South Lancashire Regiment 1881-1958. The Lancashire Regiment 1958-1970. Display includes uniforms, badges, accoutrements, medals and other relics from 1771 onwards. Comprehensive Regimental records, medal rolls and war diaries.

South Nottingham Hussars Yeomanry

T.A. Centre
Hucknall Lane
Bulwell
Nottingham NG6 8AQ

Tel: 0602 272251

South Somerset District Council Museum

Hendford
Yeovil
Somerset

Tel: 0935 24774

St Peter's Bunker Museum

St Peter's Village
St Peter
Jersey
Channel Islands

Contact: Mrs Anita Mayne

Tel: 0534 81048

Staff College Museum

Camberley
Surrey GU15 4NP

Contact: Colonel P.S. Newton

Tel: 0276 63344 X2602

Deals with the history and dress of the staff of the British Army since the formation of the Staff College in 1799. Visitors by appointment only.

Stirling Regimental Museum

Stirling Castle
Stirling FK8 1EJ

Tel: 0786 75165

Suffolk Regimental Museum

The Keep, Gibraltar Barracks
Out Risbygate Street
Bury St Edmunds
Suffolk LP33 3RN

Tel: 0284 2394

Sussex Combined Services Museum

Redoubt Fortress
Royal Parade
Eastbourne
Sussex BN22 7AQ

Tel: 0323 35809

Swindon Museum & Art Gallery

Bath Road
Swindon
Wiltshire

Tel: 0793 26161

Tenby Museum

Castle Hill
Tenby
Pembrokeshire
Dyfed

Tel: 0834 2908

The Army Museums Ogilby Trust

Connaught Barracks
Duke of Connaught Road
Aldershot GU11 2LR

Tel: 0252 331393

The Black Watch Museum
Balhousie Castle
Perth

Tel: 0738 21281

The Buffs Regimental Museum
The Royal Museum
High Street
Canterbury
Kent CT1 2JE

Tel: 0227 452747

The Burrell Collection
Pollok Country Farm
2060 Pollokshaws Road
Glasgow G43 1AT

Tel: 041 649 7151

The Devonshire Regiment Mus
Wyvern Barracks
Barrack Road
Exeter
Devon EX2 6AE

Tel: 0392 218178

The Green Howards Museum
Trinity Church Square
Richmond
Yorkshire DL10 4QN

Tel: 0748 2133

The Grosvenor Museum
27 Grosvenor Street
Chester CH1 2DD

Tel: 0244 21616

The Huntcliff Garrison
4 Southern road
Cowlersley
Huddersfield HD4 5TJ

Contact: Phillip Cadogan

Tel: 0484 647717

The Hunterian Museum
Glasgow University
Glasgow G12 8QQ

Tel: 041 339 8855

The Invasion Museum
The Wish Tower
King Edward's Parade
Eastbourne
Sussex BN21 4BY

Tel: 0323 35809

The Military Heritage Museum
West Street
Lewes
Sussex BN7 2NJ

Contact: Roy Butler

Tel: 0273 473137

Collection of Military History, 1660–1914, including uniforms, headdress, weapons and equipment. Admission by prior appointment only.

The National Army Museum
Royal Hospital Road
Chelsea
London SW3 4HT

Tel: 071 730 0717

The Nelson Museum
Monmouth
Gwent

The Polish Institute & Sikorski Museum
20 Princes Gate
London SW7

Tel: 071 589 9249

The Queen's Lancashire Regiment
RHQ Fulwood Barracks
Preston
Lancs PR2 4AA

Contact: Major A.J. Mather

Tel: 0772 716543 X2362

Contains uniforms, arms, equipment, medals and military artefacts pertaining to The Loyal Regiment.

The Queen's Regimental Museum
Inner Bailey
Dover Castle
Dover
Kent

Tel: 0304 24021

The Royal Fusiliers Museum
H.M. Tower of London
London EC3N 4AB

Tel: 071 709 0765

The Royal Green Jackets Museum
Peninsular Barracks
Romsey Road
Winchester
Hampshire SO23 8TS

Contact: The Curator

Tel: 0962 863846

Regimental museum for The Oxfordshire and Buckinghamshire Light Infantry, The King's Royal Rifle Corps and The Rifle Brigade. The Waterloo Diorama has twenty thousand model figures and a sound and light commentary. For further details contact the museum.

The Royal Hampshire Regiment
Museum & Memorial Garden
Serle's House, Southgate St
Winchester
Hampshire SO23 9EG

Tel: 0962 63658

The Royal Hussars Museum
TAVR Centre
Lower Barracks, Southgate St
Winchester
Hampshire

Tel: 0962 63751

The Royal Norfolk Reg Museum
Britannia Barracks
Norfolk NR1 4HJ

Tel: 0603 628455

The Royal Warwickshire Regimental Museum
St. John's House
Warwick

Tel: 0926 491653

The Sherwood Foresters Museum
The Castle
Nottingham NG1 6EL

Tel: 0602 785516

The Shropshire Regimental Museum
The Castle
Shrewsbury
Shropshire SY1 2AT

Contact: Mr G. Archer Parfitt

Tel: 0743 358516

The collections of The King's Shropshire Light Infantry, The Shropshire Yeomanry Cavalry and The Shropshire Royal Horse Artillery are housed in Shrewsbury Castle which dates from 1083. Open Mon–Sun, 10.00am–5.00pm (Sun, Easter–Oct only), last admission 4.00pm.

The Shuttleworth Collection
Old Warden Aerodrome
Biggleswade
Beds SG18 9EP

Tel: 0767 27288

The Tank Museum
Bovington Camp
Wareham
Dorset BH20 6JG

Contact: George Forty

Tel: 0929 403463
Fax: 0929 405360

Located at Bovington Camp, near Wool (British Rail), Dorset. One of the world's largest and most comprehensive armoured fighting vehicle collections. The library, photographic and plans archive is vast! The shop and mail order service sell a wide range of military books, models and model kits – send s.a.e for details. Open daily 10.00am–5.00pm except 10 days at Christmas. 1992 admission charges:– Adults £4.00, Children/OAP £2.00. Large free coach and car parks, 150 seat licensed self-service restaurant, picnic area and many other features. Regular military events held every year. A must for any modeller, wargamer and military enthusiast!

The Warnham War Museum
Durfold Hill
Warnham
Horsham
Sussex

Tel: 0403 65607

The Welsh Regiment Museum
The Black & Barbican Towers
Cardiff Castle
Cardiff
Glamorgan CF1 2RB

Contact: The Curator

Tel: 0222 229367

Houses exhibits commemorating The Welch Regiment (41st & 69th Foot) 1719–1969, The Militia and Volunteers of South Wales (41st Regimental District), 1794–1908 and the Services of the Royal Regiment of Wales 1969 to present day. Open daily 10.00am–4.00pm.

The Worcestershire Regimental Museum
Worcester City Museum
Foregate Street
Worcester WR1 1DT

Tel: 0905 25371

The York and Lancaster Regimental Museum
Central Library and Arts Cntr
Walker Place
Rotherham
South Yorkshire S65 1JH

Contact: The Curator

Tel: 0709 382121 X3625

The museum conveys a history of The Regiment and its forbears, The 65th and 84th Regiments of Foot (1758–1968) including Militia, Rifle Volunteers and Territorials. Open Tues–Sat, 10.00am–5.00pm. Free admission. Regimental archive by appointment. Bar, cafe, parking.

Torbay Aircraft Museum
Higher Blagdon
Nr. Paignton
Devon TQ3 3YG

Tel: 0803 553540

Towneley Hall Art Gallery
Towneley Hall
Burnley
Lancs BB11 3RQ

Exhibits relating to The East Lancashire Regiment.

Victoria & Albert Museum
South Kensington
London SW7 2RL

Tel: 071 589 6371

Wallace Collection
Hertford House
Manchester Square
London W1M 6BN

Tel: 071 935 0687

Walmer Castle
Deal
Kent

Warwickshire Yeomanry
The Court House
Jury Street
Warwick CV34 4EW

Tel: 0926 492212

Weapons Museum
School of Infantry
Warminster
Wiltshire BA12 0DJ

Tel: 0985 214000

Wellington Museum
Apsley House
149 Piccadilly
London W1V 9FA

Tel: 071 499 5676

West Highland Museum
Cameron Square
Fort William
Inverness–shire

Tel: 0397 2169

Westminster & Berkshire Dragoons Museum
R.H.Q.
1 Elverton Street
London SW1P 2QJ

Tel: 071 834 3537

Westmoreland & Cumberland Yeomanry Mus.
Dalemain
Nr Penrith
Cumbria

Tel: 085 36 450

Antiques & Prints

Andrew Butler Insignia
10 Chatham Street
Ramsgate
Kent CT11 7PP

Tel: 0843 67816

Battle Orders
7 Eastbourne Road
L.Willingdon
Eastbourne
East Sussex BN20 9NR

Tel: 0323 125182

Bennett, Ray
Warwick Cottage
Pikedam Lane, Fleet
Holbeach
Sth Lincoln PE12 8QT

Bloxham, Richard
15 Trevor Road
Hinckley
Leics LE10 1JD

Tel: 0455 635644

Blunderbuss Antiques
29 Thayer Street
London W1M 5LJ

Tel: 071 486 2444

Brindley, John
29 Hambledon Road
Clanfield
Hampshire PO8 0QU

Bryant & Gwynn Antiques
8 Drayton Lane
Drayton Bassett
Staffordshire B78 3TZ

Contact: David Bryant & Paul Gwynn

Tel: 0827 289956

All types of military uniforms, medals, swords and militaria supplied. Also deactivated military arms and muskets. Items not stocked can be ordered and traced.

Burland Fine Art U.K. Ltd
Highgate Street
Hunslet
Leeds
West Yorkshire LS10 1QR

Tel: 0532 760437

Castita Designs
55a Castle Street
Truro
Cornwall TR1 3AF

Tel: 0872 77413

Castle Armoury
London Road
Stretton-on-Dunsmore
Rugby
Warwickshire CV23 9HX

Central Arms Fairs
11 Berwick Close
Warwick
Warwickshire CV34 5UF

Contact: Chris James

Tel: 0926 497340

Organiser of events for arms, medal & militaria collectors at Cheltenham and Winchester with 70–100 stands present. Also produces the Arms Fair Calendar giving details of all major events in the U.K.. 1992 issue £4.50.

Cranston Fine Arts
Torwood House
Torwood Hill Road
Rhu, Helensburgh
Dumbartonshire G84 8LE

Contact: David Higgins

Tel: 0436 820269
Fax: 0436 820473

Publishers of military prints taken from original regimental paintings and art galleries around the world. Over 120 prints from The Napoleonic Wars, Crimean, English Civil War, American War of Independance, American Civil War, Zulu, Boer, WWI and other colonial wars.

C.J. & A.Dixon Ltd
23 Prospect Street
Bridlington
Yorkshire

Tel: 0262 676877

Dunelme Coins & Medals
County Collectors Centre
7 Durham Road
Esh Winning
Durham DH7 9NW

Contact: Peter G Smith

Tel: 091 373 4446
Fax: 091 373 6368

Dealers in war and campaign medals (medal ribbons stocked), regimental badges, historical documents and autographed letters. Also coins and banknotes of the world. Open Mon–Sat 9.00am–5.00pm (closed Wed).

Fine Detail Art
The Studio
80 Westgate St
Gloucester GL1 2NZ

Tel: 0452 713057

Forbes & Thomson
Burgate Antiques Centre
10c Burgate
Canterbury
Kent

Contact: Rowena Forbes/Thelma Thomson

Tel: 081 688 6698

Specialist dealers in old toy soldiers by Britains, Johillco etc. and related lead and tinplate toys. Model soldiers & kits by Rose Models and Chota Sahib. Painted military miniature figures. Mail order and office address, P.O. Box 375, South Croydon, CR2 6ZG. Open Mon–Sat 10.00am–5.00pm.

Frontispiece
40 Porters Walk
Tobacco Dock, Pennington St
London E1 9SF

Contact: Reginald Beer

Tel: 071 702 1678

See advertisement facing introduction

Gallery Militaire
1 Holstock Road
Ilford
Essex IG1 1LG

Contact: Rodney Gander

Tel: 081 478 8383
Fax: 081 553 4331

Fine and investment art dealers and publishers, supplying original paintings, limited edition prints, reproductions, plates and postcards. All types of framing and art commissions undertaken. European dealers and distributors for major military artists. Gallery viewing by appointment. Mail order. Large A4 illustrated catalogue £3.00 UK, £4.00 Europe $10.00 USA Airmail.

See advertisement in colour section

Geoff White Ltd.
Rushmoor Lane
Blackwell
Bristol BS19 3JA

Tel: 0275 462346

Publishers of military postcards, collectors cards, prints and other related material. All items are designed to supply reference material for collectors, modellers and other enthusiasts. Send s.a.e. for illustrated catalogue.

Granta Stamp & Coin Shop
28 Magdalene Street
Cambridge

Tel: 0223 315044

J.C. Mummery
16 Northumberland Crescent
Bedfont
Middx TW14 9SZ

Contact: John Mummery

Tel: 081 751 4599

Publisher and dealer in military pictures and prints, hand coloured engravings, varnish texturing and custom framing. Mail order facility, lists on request. Personal visitors by arrangements.

Kent Sales
The Barn, 'Giffords'
Homesdale Road
South Darenth
Kent DA4 9AF

Tel: 0322 864919

Lapworth, Mike
109 Reedley Road
Bristol BS9 1BE

Legionnaires
Golden Hill Fort
Freshwater
Isle of Wight PO40 9TF

Manton International Arms
140 Bromsgrove Street
Birmingham B5 6RG

Tel: 021 666 6066

Milan Armouries
Peldon Lodge Farm
Lodge Lane
Peldon
Essex CO5 7PZ

Tel: 020 635 661

Military Antiques
Shop 3, Phelps Cottage
357 Upper Street
London N1 0PD

Tel: 071 359 2224

Military Antiques is situated in the heart of Camden Passage, one of London's leading antique areas. They have been established in the area for a number of years and are well known to collectors at home and abroad. They specialise in WWI and WWII uniforms, equipment, awards, helmets, daggers and swords. Also many unique and interesting items for the collector, investor or museum. All items are original and carry a full money back cover. They produce an illustrated catalogue twice a year at a charge of £3.00 per copy. Any 'wants' lists welcome and they will endeavour to locate items. They also hire items for the entertainment industry.

Opening times are Tues–Fri 11.00am–5.00pm, Sat 10.00am–5.00pm. Closed on Sundays and Mondays. If travelling some distance they advise a phone call first. Military Antiques invite you call in and see them next time you are visiting London.

Military & Oriental Ltd.
749 Abbeydale Road
Sheffield
Yorks S7 2BG

Tel: 0742 550536

Suppliers of all militaria, military and historical books. Medal replacement service. Military prints. Regimental ties and blazer badges. Restoration of military antiques. Medal research facility. Medal framing service. Rare and quality military books.

Museum of the Royal Scots Dragoon Guard
The Castle
Edinburgh EH1 2YT

Contact: Lt Col J.L. Wilson Smith

Tel: 031 336 1761 X4265

Regimental museum telling history of The Royal Scots. Museum shop selling regimental souvenirs, badges, buttons etc. Send s.a.e. for list. Open Mon–Sat 9.30am–4.00pm, Sun 11.30am–4.00pm, closed weekends October to March.

Opperman, George
Flat 12
110/112 Bath Road
Cheltenham
Glos GL35 7JX

Contact: George Opperman

Private collector with large collection to sell. 50,000 lead soldiers, military books and magazines, post and cigarette cards. Send s.a.e. and 3 x 1st class stamps for lists. Mail order only.

Picton Publishing Ltd.
Queensbridge Cottages
Patterdown
Chippenham
Wiltshire SN15 2NS

Contact: David Picton-Phillips

Tel: 0249 443430
Fax: 0249 443024

Publishers of military and local history. Mail order of new and second hand books. Fine art prints. Catalogue by request with a 50p stamp. Office hours 10.00am–5.00pm. 24hr Fax. No callers. Visa, Access.

RMK Fine Prints
13 Keere Street
Lewes
Sussex BN7 1TY

Ransome, Allan
43 Brookfield Avenue
Timperley
Altrincham
Cheshire WA15 6TH

Regimentals
70 Essex Road
Islington
London N1 8LT

Tel: 071 359 8579
Fax: 071 704 0879

Large stock of militaria including British Victorian head dress and badges, WWI and WWII German items, Royal Flying Corps and aviation artifacts, military firearms, antique pistols, Japanese swords etc. Colour illustrated catalogue bi-annually published and costs £13.50p. Open Tues–Sat, 10.00am–5.00pm

See advertisement facing contents page.

Royal Marines Museum
Southsea
Portsmouth
Hampshire PO4 9PX

Tel: 0705 819385/831679
Fax: 0705 838420

The history of the Marines since 1664 to the present day, incorporating medal, uniform and weapon collections. Library and archive research facilities available by appointment. Photographic library with copying service. Museum shop with mail order department. Open Mon–Sun, 10am–4.40pm.

Royal Rose Badge Company
'Ingleside'
Barehams Lane
Quadring
Lincolnshire PE11 4PX

Sabre, A.
Higher Brinscott
Greenham
Wellington
Somerset TA21 8QE

Seidler, C.F.
Grays-in-the-Mews Antique Mrkt
1-7 Davies Mews, Davies Street
London W1V 1AA

Contact: C.F. Seidler

Tel: 071 629 2851

(Entry continued on page 46)

C.F. Seidler specialises in the following areas:

1. American, British and European edged weapons c.1550–1945.
2. American, British and European antique firearms.
3. American, British and European medals, orders and decorations c.1815 to date.
4. British and European uniform items 19th and early 20thcentury.
5. British truncheons and tipstaves 18th and 19th century.
6. British and European military watercolours and prints 18th and 19th century.
7. British regimental histories and army lists 18th to 20th century.
8. World-wide horse furniture: bridles, bits, spurs, stirrups (to early 20th century only).
9. Japanese and Oriental arms and armour.
10. Aeronautical prizes – early 20th century.

C.F. Seidler is keen to purchase any of the above items at competitive prices and will sell on a consignment or commission basis. Valuation for probate and insurance gladly undertaken. Does not issue a catalogue but will gladly receive clients' wants lists.

Open Mon–Fri, 11.00am–6.00pm. Nearest tube station Bond Street (Central line).

Space City Gifts
33 Marine Terrace
Margate
Kent CT9 1XJ

Tel: 0843 294906

Studio 'Cae Coch Bach'
Seion
Rhosgoch
Anglesey
Gwynedd LL66 0AE

Tenniswood, Jeremy
28 Gordon Road
Aldershot
Hampshire GU11 1ND

Tel: 0252 319791
Fax: 0252 342339

The Collectors Market
London Bridge BR Station

Tel: 081 398 8065

Over 60 stands including medal dealers, badges and militaria on the concourse of London Bridge Main Line Station every Saturday.

The London Militaria Market
Angel Arcade
Camden Passage
London N1

Tel: 063 882 2503

Over 30 stands dealing in all types of badges, bayonets, brooches, buttons, helmets, medals, postcards, swords, uniforms and many other military collectables. Every Sat 8.00am–2.00pm.

The Mad Colonel
37 Mildmay Park
Islington
London N1 4NA

Contact: Marc St. Clare

Tel: 071 354 3259

Supplier of military items from original sources. Commissions undertaken. Extensive search capability. Large network provides toy soldiers, ship and aircraft models, new and antique dinky toys. All military collectables and curios bought and sold. Write or phone with requirements.

The Pompadour Gallery
PO Box 11
Romford
Essex RM7 7HY

Contact: George Newark

Tel: 0708 723742

Publishers of full colour military postcards reproduced from original paintings by Bryan Fosten, Harry Payne, Lady Butler, R.Caton Woodville illustrating uniforms of British and foreign armies and police forces. Each set contains six postcards and the following sets are now available at £3.00 per set including postage. U.S.A. $7.00 per set including postage.
Volunteer Regiments of London
Uniforms of the British Empire
Military Units of Essex
Paintings by R.Caton Woodville
The Royal Yeomanry
Uniforms of The Royal Navy
Regiments of Canada
Italian Carabinieri
17/21st Lancers
Military art of Harry Payne
Royal Canadian Mounted Police
United States Marine Corps
Paintings by Lady Butler
New York City Police Department
Grenadier Guards
Corps of Royal Military Police
London's Metropolitan Police
Inns of Court Regiment
Kipling's Soldiers

The Black Watch (R.H.R.)
French Foreign Legion
London Fire Brigade
Royal Scots Dragoon Guards
R.A.F. Aircrew Clothing 1918–88
Send s.a.e. for illustrated list.

The Scarlet Gunner
Post House
Stoke
Nr Andover
Hants SP11 0ND

Tony Jackson & Associates
58 Clocktower Place
North Road
London N7 9DY

Contact: Tony Jackson

Tel: 071 609 7666
Fax: 071 607 0587

Publishers of high quality limited edition and open edition military historical prints.

See advertisement in colour section

Tradition
2 Shepherd Street
Mayfair
London W1Y 7LN

Tel: 071 493 7452
Fax: 071 355 1224

One of the longest established manufacturers and retailers in the model soldier field, its London showrooms a Mecca for many collectors. Painted and unpainted figures are available in all popular scales 54mm, 90mm and 110mm, with armies from the ancient world to the present day. Troops of the Napoleonic wars and the British army through the ages are a speciality. Also manufacturer of over 200 different toy soldier boxed sets with new releases every month, which are also available unpainted. In the smaller scales 25mm & 30mm figures are made, including the famous 'Willie' range for dioramas. Open Mon–Fri 9.00am–5.30pm, Sat 9.30am–3.00pm. Catalogues are available for all sizes.

Tradition at 10 Whitehorse Street, W.1. (071 491 7077) specialises in pre-1914 militaria including uniforms, prints and paintings. Open by appointment.

Vincent, Garth
The Old Manor House
Allington
Nr Grantham
Lincolnshire

Tel: 0400 81358

Auction Houses

Bonhams
Monpelier Street
London SW7 1HH

Tel: 071 584 9161

Buckland Dix & Wood
17 Piccadilly Arcade
Piccadilly
London SW1Y 6NH

Tel: 071 493 5082
Fax: 071 499 4422

Christie's
85 Old Brompton Road
London SW7 3LD

Tel: 071 581 7611

Head Office:
8 King Street
St James's
London SW1
Tel: 071 839 9060

City Office:
50–60 Gresham Street
London EC2
Tel: 071 588 4424

Gallery Militaire
6 Holstock Road
Ilford
Essex IG1 1LG

Contact: Rodney Gander

Tel: 081 478 8383
Fax: 081 553 4331

Fine and investment art dealers and publishers, supplying original paintings, limited edition prints, reproductions, plates and postcards. All types of framing and art commissions undertaken. European dealers and distributors for major military artists. Gallery viewing by appointment. Mail order. Large A4 illustrated catalogue £3.00 UK, £4.00 Europe $10.00 USA Airmail.

See advertisement in colour section

Glendining's
101 New Bond Street
London W1Y 9LG

Contact: Daniel Fearon

Tel: 071 493 2445
Fax: 071 491 9181

Kent Sales
Kent House
New Road
South Darenth
Kent DA4 9AR

Phillips
7 Blenheim Street
New Bond Street
London W1Y 0AS

Tel: 071 629 6602

Scorpio
50 High Street
Battle
Battle
E.Sussex TN33 0EN

Sotheby's
34–35 New Bond Street
London W1A 2AA

Tel: 071 493 8080

Sotheby's
Summers Place
Nr Billinghurst
West Sussex RH14 9AD

Tel: 040381 3933

Spink & Son Ltd.
5 King Street
St James's
London SW1Y 6QS

Contact: Andrew Litherland

Tel: 071 930 7888
Fax: 071 839 4853

Extensive stock of orders, decorations and medals. Spinks publish numismatic reference books and a monthly sales list 'The Numismatic Circular'. Regular auctions held and comprehensive medal display service offered. Mon–Fri 9.30am–5.30pm.

Wallis & Wallis
West Street Auction Galleries
Lewes
Sussex BN7 2NJ

Contact: Roy Butler

Tel: 0273 480208
Fax: 0273 476562

Specialist auctioneers of arms, armour, militaria, medals. Nine regular, two regular two day sales per year with Spring and Autumn connoisseur collector's sales. Sales catalogues (including U.K. postage):

Arms, armour. £4.50 Militaria, medals.£4.50

Connoisseur Collector's (full colour). £12.50

Postal bids welcome. Open Mon–Fri, 9.00am–5.00pm.

Weller & Dufty Ltd.
141 Bromsgrove Street
Birmingham 5

Tel: 021 692 1414

Uniforms, Armour & Insignia

Andrew Butler Insignia
10 Chatham Street
Ramsgate
Kent CT11 7PP

Tel: 0843 67816

Brannagan, R.J.
115 Bonaccord Street
Aberdeen

Tel: 0224 572826

Bryant & Gwynn Antiques
8 Drayton Lane
Drayton Bassett
Staffordshire B78 3TZ

Contact: David Bryant & Paul Gwynn

Tel: 0827 289956

All types of military uniforms, medals, swords and militaria supplied. Also deactivated military arms and muskets. Items not stocked can be ordered and traced.

Cairncross and Sons
31 Belle Vue Street
Filey
North Yorkshire YO14 9HU

Contact: George Cairncross

Tel: 0723 513287

Castle Armoury
London Road
Stretton–on–Dunsmore
Rugby
Warwickshire CV23 9HX

Castle Armoury
London Road
Dover
Kent CT1 0SS

Central Antique Arms & Militaria
Smith Street Antique Centre
7 Smith Street
Warwick
Warwickshire CV34 4JA

Contact: Chris James

Tel: 0926 400554

Buys and sells antique guns, swords, bayonets, helmets, badges, British and German medals and decorations, original Third Reich militaria and documents. Send for illustrated catalogue 10 x 1st class stamps. Shop open Mon–Sat, 10.00am–5.00pm. Exhibits at most major arms fairs.

Central Arms Fairs
11 Berwick Close
Warwick
Warwickshire CV34 5UF

Contact: Chris James

Tel: 0926 497340

Organiser of events for arms, medal & militaria collectors at Cheltenham and Winchester with 70–100 stands present. Also produces the Arms Fair Calendar giving details of all major events in the U.K.. 1992 issue £4.50.

Clark, Brian
16 Lothian Road
Middlesborough
Cleveland TS4 2HR

Tel: 0642 240827

Coldstream Military Antiques
55a High Street
Marlow
Bucks SL7 1BA

Contact: Steven Bosley

Tel: 0628 822503
Fax: 0628 822503

Postal service only. Large selection of original British full dress helmets, lance caps, helmet plates, cap badges, formation signs, regimental brooches etc. No general catalogue but 'wants' lists welcome. All items are guaranteed genuine. Visa & Mastercard.

Corridors of Time
11 Mulberry Court
Pagham
West Sussex PO21 4TP

Contact: Alan Jeffrey

Tel: 0243 262291
Fax: 0243 262291

See description under **Re–enactors**

C.J. & A. Dixon Ltd.
23 Prospect Street
Bridlington
Yorks YO15 2AE

Contact: Christopher Dixon

Tel: 0262 676877
Fax: 0262 606600

Stockists of British and foreign orders, decorations, war medals, ribbons, mounting and display cases. Sales catalogues £2.00 each or £3.00 for 3 issues including postage U.K.. Over 1000 items in every catalogue. Mail order specialists. Open Mon–Sat, 10.00am–4.30pm.

Dunelme Coins & Medals
County Collectors Centre
7 Durham Road
Esh Winning
Durham DH7 9NW

Contact: Peter G Smith

Tel: 091 373 4446
Fax: 091 373 6368

Dealers in war and campaign medals (medal ribbons stocked), regimental badges, historical documents and autographed letters. Also coins and banknotes of the world. Open Mon–Sat 9.00am–5.00pm (closed Wed).

East Bloc Militaria
280 Silverdale Road
Reading
Berks RG6 2NU

Contact: Michael Passmore

Tel: 0734 351381

Specialises in East German and Soviet Forces insignia, medals and uniforms. Unusual and rare items available. Mail order only. Search service provided. Send s.a.e. for free list. Phone evenings and weekends only.

Glendining's
101 New Bond Street
London W1Y 9LG

Contact: Daniel Fearon

Tel: 071 493 2445
Fax: 071 491 9181

Gryphon Trading
PO Box 5
Ripon
North Yorkshire HG4 3YR

Contact: Paul Cordle

Tel: 0765 690216
Fax: 0765 690702

Individual mail orders or large discounted orders accepted for badged regimental pewter. Moulds for badges (cast in solid pewter) are taken from existing metal badges or a new 'master' badge sculpted to order. Send large s.a.e. for catalogue.

Historical Reproductions

Sussex Farm Museum
Manor Farm
Horam, Nr Heathfield
E.Sussex TN21 0JB

Contact: Roy King

Reproduction armourer, helmets, edged weapons and some associated goods. Theatrical and film props, cannons, siege engines etc. Pyrotechnic service for simulated battles available. Mail order, limited catalogue available – most items made to order. Visitors by appointment only. Surrounding fields and Farm Museum available for location hire.

M & T Militaria

The Banks
Banks Lane, Victoria Road
Carlisle
Cumbria CA1 2UA

Contact: Malcolm Bowers

Tel: 0228 31988

Specialists in original Third Reich militaria. Regular mail order catalogue with over 700 items. List subscriptions of £4.00 per year for 4 guaranteed copies.

Military Antiques

Shop 3, Phelps Cottage
357 Upper Street
London N1 0PD

Tel: 071 359 2224

See description under **Antiques & Prints.**

Military & Oriental Ltd.

749 Abbeydale Road
Sheffield
Yorks S7 2BG

Tel: 0742 550536

Suppliers of all militaria, military and historical books. Medal replacement service. Military prints. Regimental ties and blazer badges. Restoration of military antiques. Medal research facility. Medal framing service. Rare and quality military books.

Morigi, Nicholas

14 Seacroft Road
Broadstairs
Kent CT10 1TL

Contact: Nicholas Morigi

Tel: 0843 602243
Fax: 0843 603940 F

Specialist in cloth and metal insignia of all countries from 1900 to present day. Specialising in WWII, Vietnam and current. Countries represented include Great Britain, United States, Third Reich Germany, Soviet Union and France. Mail order only. Wholesale enquiries are also welcome. Full colour catalogue £3.00.

Museum of the Royal Scots Dragoon Guard

The Castle
Edinburgh EH1 2YT

Contact: Lt Col J.L. Wilson Smith

Tel: 031 336 1761 X4265

Regimental museum telling history of The Royal Scots. Museum shop selling regimental souvenirs, badges, buttons etc. Send s.a.e. for list. Open Mon–Sat 9.30am–4.00pm, Sun 11.30am–4.00pm, closed weekends October to March.

Pastimes

22/23 Lower Park Road
Bristol
Avon

Contact: Andy Stevens

Tel: 0272 299330

Deals in general militaria, medals and secondhand military books. Especially wanted are items and medals of any Bristol or Gloucestershire Volunteer Units. Open Mon–Sat, 10.30pm–5.00pm (Wed 11.00am). Advises to ring before visiting.

Raven Armoury

Handleys Farm
Dunmow Road, Thaxted
Dunmow
Essex CM6 2NX

Contact: Simon Fearnhamm

Tel: 0371 870486
Fax: 0371 870486

Handcrafted swords, chainmail and armour for collectors and re-enactors. Sword range includes historical reproductions on display at The Royal Armouries Shop in The Tower of London. Fully guaranteed.

Regimentals

70 Essex Road
Islington
London N1 8LT

Tel: 071 359 8579
Fax: 071 704 0879

Large stock of militaria including British Victorian head dress and badges, WWI and WWII German items, Royal Flying Corps and aviation artifacts, military firearms, antique pistols, Japanese swords etc. Colour illustrated catalogue bi-annually published and costs £13.50p. Open Tues–Sat, 10.00am–5.00pm.

See advertisement facing Title page

Richard Dunk (Armourer)

23 Overhill Road
Burntwood
Walsall
West Midlands WS7 8SU

Royal Armouries

H.M. Tower of London
London EC3 4AB

Tel: 071 480 6358

The Royal Armouries, HM Tower of London, is the national museum of arms and armour. The collection includes pieces from the Dark Ages to the present day including sporting armours of Henry VIII and Charles I, a hunting and sporting collection, an oriental armoury and an extensive British military 18th & 19th century collection. Admission with Tower ticket. Open Mar–Oct, Mon–Sat 9.30am–5.45.pm, Sun 2.00pm–5.30pm; Nov–Feb Mon–Sat 9.30am–4.30pm, closed Sun. Underground Circle and District to Tower Hill. Bus 15, 42, 78. Riverboat to Tower Pier. Shop, mail order for specialist books and videos, arms and armour replicas, catalogue and newsletter for products and adult education courses available.

Seidler, C.F.

Grays-in-the-Mews Antique Mrkt
1–7 Davies Mews, Davies Street
London W1V 1AA

Contact: C.F. Seidler

Tel: 071 629 2851

C.F. Seidler specialises in the following areas:
1. American, British and European edged weapons c.1550–1945.
2. American, British and European antique firearms.
3. American, British and European medals, orders and decorations c.1815 to date.
4. British and European uniform items 19th and early 20th century.
5. British truncheons and tipstaves 18th and 19th century.
6. British and European military watercolours and prints 18th and 19th century.

7. British regimental histories and army lists 18th to 20th century.

8. World-wide horse furniture: bridles, bits, spurs, stirrups (to early 20th century only).

9. Japanese and Oriental arms and armour.

10. Aeronautical prizes – early 20th century.

C.F. Seidler is keen to purchase any of the above items at competitive prices and will sell on a consignment or commission basis. Valuation for probate and insurance gladly undertaken. Does not issue a catalogue but will gladly receive clients' wants lists.

Open Mon–Fri, 11.00am–6.00pm. Nearest tube station Bond Street (Central line).

Soldier of Fortune
Unit 3a–b Brymau 3 Estate
River Lane, Saltney
Chester CH4 8RQ

Contact: Peter Kabluczenko

Tel: 0244 681090
Fax: 0244 674651

Specialising in U.S. Forces – modern and Vietnam – clothing and equipment. Also stocks British, West and East German, Belgium, Austrian, French and S.W.A.T. equipment, books, replica and deactivated guns, outdoor and survival. 32 page catalogue available at £1.00. Military showroom at Slatney, visit by appointment only. Shops: 56 Lower Bridge St., Chester. 56 Richmond St., Liverpool.

See advertisement in colour section

Spink & Son Ltd.
5 King Street
St James's
London SW1Y 6QS

Contact: Andrew Litherland

Tel: 071 930 7888
Fax: 071 839 4853

Extensive stock of orders, decorations and medals. Spinks publish numismatic reference books and a monthly sales list 'The Numismatic Circular'. Regular auctions held and comprehensive medal display service offered. Mon–Fri 9.30am–5.30pm.

Steve Johnson Militaria
PO Box 37
Gosforth
Newcastle–Upon–Tyne NE3 1RE

Tel: 091 473 9274

Sunset Militaria
Dinedor Cross
Herefordshire HR2 6PF

Contact: David Seeney

Tel: 0432 870 420

Genuine militaria (money back guarantee) headdress, collar badges, titles, formation, trade, foreign badges, buttons, medals, miniature medals, world ribbons, mess badges, special forces, aviation, equipment, uniforms, deactivated weapons, books, photos. Send large s.a.e., stating interests, for sample list (mail order only).

Syntown Militaria International
Westway
Rectory Lane
Winchelsea
East Sussex TN36 4EY

Contact: Christopher Coxon

Tel: 0797 223388
Fax: 0797 224834

Stockists of high quality reproduction and original uniforms, equipment and soldiers personal small kit from WWII, exact repro German camo garments a speciality, axis and allied lists bi-monthly £1.00 each. Access, Visa and Diners Club by post or phone.

The Armoury of St. James
17 Piccadilly Arcade
Piccadilly
London SW1Y 6NH

Contact: Mark St. Clair

The Collectors Market
London Bridge BR Station

Tel: 081 398 8065

Over 60 stands including medal dealers, badges and militaria on the concourse of London Bridge Main Line Station every Saturday.

The London Militaria Market
Angel Arcade
Camden Passage
London N1

Tel: 063 882 2503

Over 30 stands dealing in all types of badges, bayonets, brooches, buttons, helmets, medals, postcards, swords, uniforms and many other military collectables. Every Sat 8.00am–2.00pm.

The Mad Colonel
37 Mildmay Park
Islington
London N1 4NA

Contact: Marc St. Clare

Tel: 071 354 3259

Supplier of military items from original sources. Commissions undertaken. Extensive search capability. Large network provides toy soldiers, ship and aircraft models, new and antique dinky toys. All military collectables and curios bought and sold. Write or phone with requirements.

The Military Heritage Museum
West Street
Lewes
Sussex BN7 2NJ

Contact: Roy Butler

Tel: 0273 473137

Collection of Military History, 1660–1914, including uniforms, headdress, weapons and equipment. Admission by prior appointment only.

The Regia Anglorum
9 Durleigh Close
Headley Park
Bristol
Avon BS13 7NQ

Contact: J K Siddorn

Tel: 0271 646818
Fax: 0272 646818

An international society, well-known as the principal recreator of the life and times of the folk of these islands in the hundred years preceding the Norman Conquest. They have resident specialists to advise on all aspects of authentic recreation, conducting research to the highest standards. Fully narrated battle re-enactments, often involving around two hundred combatants, create living images of those times. Their tented 'living history' exhibit, the largest and most comprehensive of its kind anywhere, is separately crewed by trained specialist personnel. Also suppliers of props, costume and specialist extras for film and TV.

The Tank Museum
Bovington Camp
Wareham
Dorset BH20 6JG

Contact: George Forty

Tel: 0929 403463
Fax: 0929 405360

See description under **Museums**

Tradition

2 Shepherd Street
Mayfair
London W1Y 7LN

Tel: 071 493 7452
Fax: 071 355 1224

One of the longest established manufacturers and retailers in the model soldier field, its London showrooms a Mecca for many collectors. Painted and unpainted figures are available in all popular scales 54mm, 90mm and 110mm, with armies from the ancient world to the present day. Troops of the Napoleonic wars and the British army through the ages are a speciality. Also manufacturer of over 200 different toy soldier boxed sets with new releases every month, which are also available unpainted. In the smaller scales 25mm & 30mm figures are made, including the famous 'Willie' range for dioramas. Open Mon–Fri 9.00am–5.30pm, Sat 9.30am–3.00pm. Catalogues are available for all sizes.

Tradition at 10 Whitehorse Street, W.1. (071 491 7077) specialises in pre–1914 militaria including uniforms, prints and paintings. Open by appointment.

Trafalgar Square Collectors Centre

7 Whitcomb Street
London WC2H 7HA

Contact: Raymond Holdich

Tel: 071 930 1979

A selection of British campaign and gallantry medals, British cap badges, Third Reich items, orders, medals and decorations from around the world. Full medal mounting service including court style and framing. Open Mon–Fri, 11.00am–5.30pm.

Ulric of England

6 The Glade
Stoneleigh
Epsom
Surrey KT17 2HB

Tel: 081 393 1434
Fax: 081 393 9555

Third Reich specialist.

Victory Supplies

2nd Floor
25 Victoria Street
Liverpool
Merseyside L1 6BD

Tel: 0831 520905

Stockists of coins, medals and banknotes, badges, buttons, bayonets, swords and military items. Lists issued. Callers welcome Mon–Fri, 10.00am–4.00pm. Situated in Liverpool city centre. All the above bought for cash.

See advertisement facing introduction

Wallis & Wallis

West Street Auction Galleries
Lewes
Sussex BN7 2NJ

Contact: Roy Butler

Tel: 0273 480208
Fax: 0273 476562

Specialist auctioneers of arms, armour, militaria, medals. Nine regular, two regular two day sales per year with Spring and Autumn connoisseur collector's sales. Sales catalogues (including U.K. postage):

Arms, armour. £4.50

Militaria, medals. £4.50

Connoisseur Collector's (full colour). £12.50

Postal bids welcome. Open Mon–Fri, 9.00am–5.00pm.

Wheeler, Stephen

6 Clapham Court Terrace
Kings Avenue
London SW4 8DT

Medals

Bryant & Gwynn Antiques
8 Drayton Lane
Drayton Bassett
Staffordshire B78 3TZ

Contact: David Bryant & Paul Gwynn

Tel: 0827 289956

All types of military uniforms, medals, swords and militaria supplied. Also deactivated military arms and muskets. Items not stocked can be ordered and traced.

Collett, Norman W.
PO Box 235
London SE23 1NS

Contact: Norman Collett

Tel: 081 291 1435

Established 1975, dealing in British and Commonwealth medals and in military books. Postal business only apart from presence at major medal fairs. Regular catalogues issued of both books and medals, with more than 500 items in each. Subscription per annum is £7 for booklists and £8 for medal lists.

Cotrel Medals
7 Stanton Road
Bournemouth
Dorset BH10 5DS

Contact: Peter Cotrel

Tel: 0202 516801

Mail-order company dealing in medals and related accessories. Send s.a.e. for list. Callers by appointment only. Offers made on surplus medals. Mounting service available.

C.J. & A. Dixon Ltd.
23 Prospect Street
Bridlington
Yorks YO15 2AE

Contact: Christopher Dixon

Tel: 0262 676877
Fax: 0262 606600

Stockists of British and foreign orders, decorations, war medals, ribbons, mounting and display cases. Sales catalogues £2.00 each or £3.00 for 3 issues including postage U.K.. Over 1000 items in every catalogue. Mail order specialists. Open Mon–Sat, 10.00am–4.30pm.

David Hilton Medals
38 Chetwood Drive
Widnes
Cheshire WA8 9BL

Contact: David Hilton

Tel: 051 424 0630

World medals bought and sold, 4 lists per year. Subscription £2.50 inland, £6.00 overseas. Medals sold on commission basis. Phone for details.

Dunelme Coins & Medals
County Collectors Centre
7 Durham Road
Esh Winning
Durham DH7 9NW

Contact: Peter G Smith

Tel: 091 373 4446
Fax: 091 373 6368

Dealers in war and campaign medals (medal ribbons stocked), regimental badges, historical documents and autographed letters. Also coins and banknotes of the world. Open Mon–Sat 9.00am–5.00pm (closed Wed).

East Bloc Militaria
280 Silverdale Road
Reading
Berks RG6 2NU

Contact: Michael Passmore

Tel: 0734 351381

Specialises in East German and Soviet Forces insignia, medals and uniforms. Unusual and rare items available. Mail order only. Search service provided. Send s.a.e. for free list. Phone evenings and weekends only.

Giuseppe Miceli Coin & Medal Centre
173 Wellingborough Road
Northampton NN1 4DX

Contact: Giuseppe Miceli

Tel: 0604 39776

Glendining's
101 New Bond Street
London W1Y 9LG

Contact: Daniel Fearon

Tel: 071 493 2445
Fax: 071 491 9181

Great War Medals
22 Selborne Road
London N14 7DH

Contact: M.A. Law

Tel: 081 886 4120

Large, regular mail-order listings of WWI medals and books. Purchased or sold on commission. Research services for military and family historians. Customers' specific wants advertised. O.M.R.S. member. Visa/Mastercard facility. Send s.a.e for sample catalogue.

Leroy's Miniature Medals
25 Stanfield Road
Talbot Park
Bournemouth
Dorset BH9 2NL

Contact: Michael Brachi

Tel: 0202 519090

Miniature medals, mainly early British Campaigns although also offers better quality modern medals. Also specialist in full size medals with fine quality, single British Campaign medals only. Free monthly lists available.

Military & Oriental Ltd.
749 Abbeydale Road
Sheffield
Yorks S7 2BG

Tel: 0742 550536

Suppliers of all militaria, military and historical books. Medal replacement service. Military prints. Regimental ties and blazer badges. Restoration of military antiques. Medal research facility. Medal framing service. Rare and quality military books.

Morris, Peter
1 Station Concourse
Bromley North BR Station
Bromley
Kent

Tel: 081 466 1762

Open Fri 4.30pm–8.00pm, Sat 9.00am–2.00pm and other times by arrangement. For free copy of quarterly list write to: Freepost, PO Box 223, Bromley, Kent BR1 4EQ.

M.J. & S.J. Dyas Coins/Medals
30 Shaftmoor Lane
Acocks Green
Birmingham B27 7RS

Contact: Malcolm Dyas

Tel: 021 707 2808
Fax: 021 707 5312

Operating since 1965 the company issue a total of 10 lists per year and operate a research and card index service to all their customers.

Pastimes
22/23 Lower Park Road
Bristol
Avon

Contact: Andy Stevens

Tel: 0272 299330

Deals in general militaria, medals and secondhand military books. Especially wanted are items and medals of any Bristol or Gloucestershire Volunteer Units. Open Mon–Sat, 10.30pm–5.00pm (Wed 11.00am). Advises to ring before visiting.

Roberts Medals Ltd.
6 Titan House
Cavella Park
Aldermaston
Berkshire RG7 4QW

Tel: 0734 819973
Fax: 0734 81176

Medal, book and emphera lists issued every six weeks to subscribers. Inofrmation books published for medal collectors. Callers at the Aldermaston premises are welcome – ring in advance. Specialists in Southern Africa campaigns.

See advertisement facing contents page

Romsey Medal Centre
101 The Hundred
Romsey
Hants SO51 8BY

Tel: 0794 512069

Romsey Medals
5 Bell Street
Romsey
Hants SO51 8GY

Tel: 0794 512069
Fax: 0794 830332

Seidler, C.F.
Grays–in–the–Mew Antique Mrkt
1–7 Davies Mews, Davies Street
London W1V 1AA

Contact: C.F. Seidler

Tel: 071 629 2851

C.F. Seidler specialises in the following areas:
1. American, British and European edged weapons c.1550–1945.
2. American, British and European antique firearms.
3. American, British and European medals, orders and decorations c.1815 to date.
4. British and European uniform items 19th and early 20th century.
5. British truncheons and tipstaves 18th and 19th century

6. British and European military watercolours and prints 18th and 19th century.
7. British regimental histories and army lists 18th to 20th century.
8. World–wide horse furniture: bridles, bits, spurs, stirrups (to early 20th century only).
9. Japanese and Oriental arms and armour.
10. Aeronautical prizes – early 20th century.
C.F. Seidler is keen to purchase any of the above items at competitive prices and will sell on a consignment or commission basis. Valuation for probate and insurance gladly undertaken. Does not issue a catalogue but will gladly receive clients' wants lists.
Open Mon–Fri, 11.00am–6.00pm. Nearest tube station Bond Street (Central line).

Southern Medals
16 Broom Grove
Knebworth
Herts SG3 6BQ

Contact: John Williams

Tel: 0438 811657

Selection of British and foreign orders, decorations and medals in stock. The major UK medal and militaria fairs attended. Comprehensive sales lists issued – minimum four issues per year. Subscriptions: £3.00 (UK/BFPO), £4.00 (Europe), £5.00 (elsewhere – airmail). Complimentary specimen copy sent on receipt of s.a.e./IRC.

Spink & Son Ltd.
5 King Street
St James's
London SW1Y 6QS

Contact: Andrew Litherland

Tel: 071 930 7888
Fax: 071 839 4853

Extensive stock of orders, decorations and medals. Spinks publish numismatic reference books and a monthly sales list 'The Numismatic Circular'. Regular auctions held and comprehensive medal display service offered. Mon–Fri 9.30am–5.30pm.

The Collectors Market
London Bridge BR Station

Tel: 081 398 8065

Over 60 stands including medal dealers, badges and militaria on the concourse of London Bridge Main Line Station every Saturday.

The London Militaria Market
Angel Arcade
Camden Passage
London N1

Tel: 063 882 2503

Over 30 stands dealing in all types of badges, bayonets, brooches, buttons, helmets, medals, postcards, swords, uniforms and many other military collectables. Every Sat 8.00am–2.00pm.

Toad Hall Medals
Court Road
Newton Ferrers
Nr Plymouth
South Devon PL8 1DH

Contact: Malcolm Hitchins

Tel: 0752 872672
Fax: 0752 872723

An established medal business which produces 5 to 6 lists per year, each containing several hundred constantly changing items of gallantry groups and single medals plus a good foreign section. Other sections include Nazi documents, medals and a military miscellaneous section. Send s.a.e. for latest lists.

Trafalgar Square Collectors Centre
7 Whitcomb Street
London WC2H 7HA

Contact: Raymond Holdich

Tel: 071 930 1979

A selection of British campaign and gallantry medals, British cap badges, Third Reich items, orders, medals and decorations from around the world. Full medal mounting service including court style and framing. Open Mon–Fri, 11.00am–5.30pm.

Victory Supplies
2nd Floor
25 Victoria Street
Liverpool
Merseyside L1 6BD

Tel: 0831 520905

Stockists of coins, medals and banknotes, badges, buttons, bayonets, swords and military items. Lists issued. Callers welcome Mon–Fri, 10.00am–4.00pm. Situated in Liverpool city centre. All the above bought for cash.

See advertisement facing introduction

Wallis & Wallis
West Street Auction Galleries
Lewes
Sussex BN7 2NJ

Contact: Roy Butler

Tel: 0273 480208
Fax: 0273 476562

Specialist auctioneers of arms, armour, militaria, medals. Nine regular, two regular two day sales per year with Spring and Autumn connoisseur collector's sales. Sales catalogues (including U.K. postage):
Arms, armour. £4.50
Militaria, medals.£4.50
Connoisseur Collector's (full colour). £12.50
Postal bids welcome. Open Mon–Fri, 9.00am–5.00pm.

Re-enactors

1680's Re-enactments
61 Belmont Lane
Stanmore
Middlesex HA7 2PU

Contact: Philip Nickson

17th Century Living History Heritage Ctr
25 Connaught Street
Northampton NN1 3BP

Contact: Mrs JH Thompson

21eme de Infantry of the Line
22 Swallow Street
Oldham
Lancashire OL8 4LD

Contact: Christopher Durkin

Tel: 061 652 1647

A Regiment of the Napoleonic Association dedicated to the study and recreation of the French unit during the Napoleonic period. Recruit nationwide.

24th Foot Grenadier Company
1 Cheviot Close
Risca
Gwent NP1 6RH

Contact: Colin Pearce

3rd New York Regiment
19 Treharne Road
Barry
Sth Glamorgan CF6 7QY

Contact: Michael Bailey

Tel: 0446 745936 (pm)

Recreation of the times of Captain Bruyn's Company of the Regiment. Emphasis on 'living history' displays including tactical demonstrations. The group is associated to The Society of the American Revolution and The Eagle Society.

68th Display Team
3 The Copse
Witton Le Wear
Co Durham DL14 0BA

Contact: Kelso Yuill

Tel: 088 888376

68th Regiment Light Infantry
17 Sidmouth Close
Tollesby Hall
Marton
Middlesbrough TS8 9DN

Contact: Keith Bartlett

American Civil War Society
54 Rowland Close
Cinnamon Brow
Warrington
Cheshire WA2 0DQ

Contact: Bill & Lyn Davies

Tel: 0925 818557

American Civil War re-enactments with organised weekends throughout the country. Recreating authentic camp life and battle re-enactments. Individual Regiments and artillery with authentic uniforms and equipment. Family camp available. Grand balls and social events. 'Living history' lectures, school projects. History tours of USA. Videos for sale.

Arthurian Society
5 Manor Street
Hinckley
Leics LE10 0AS

Assoc. Brittanique La Garde Imperial
8 Pippinsgreen Avenue
Kirkhamgate
Wakefield
W. Yorks

Contact: Derek Mellard

Tel: 0924 381820

Bostock Militaria
"Pinewood"
15 Waller Close
Leek Wootton
Nr Warwick
CV35 7QG

Contact: Andrew P Bostock
Fax: 17/05/91

Boston Svieter
63 Norfolk Street
Boston
Lincolnshire

Contact: Steve Dobbs

Tel: 0205 65055

Brotherhood of the Axe
29 Desborough House
Amersham Hill
High Wycombe HP13 6HH

Contact: Brin Dunsire

Call To Arms
7 Chapmans Crescent
Chesham
Buckinghamshire HP5 2QU

The Re-enactment Intersociety Newsletter. Subscriber based and solely devoted to re-enactment and the hobby's numerous branches of interest.

Cavalry Skirmish Association
55 Prestop Drive
Westfields
Ashby-de-la Zouch
Leicestershire LE6 5NA

Contact: Brian Betteridge

Tel: 0530 560164

A.C.W. re-enactment society encompassing The 7th VA and 7th MICH Cavalry. Fighting on foot and horseback. Full training given. Families welcome.

Cohors Quinta Gallorum
Arbeia Roman Fort and Museum
Baring Street
South Shields
Tyne & Wear NE33 2BB

Contact: Alexandra Croom

Tel: 091 4544093

Military and civilian re-enactment society based at Arbeia Roman Fort, for researching, reconstructing and displaying to the Public, Roman auxiliaries of the early third century fort garrison and civilians of the town. The Society mainly appears on special event days at Arbeia.

Companions of the Black Bear
1 Upper Lode Lock
Forthampton
Tewkewsbury
Gloucestershire

Contact: R F Boazman

Tel: 0684 298403

Confederate High Command
29 Grierson Close
Calne
Wiltshire SN11 8JJ

Confederate States Navy G.B.
SE Command "Redoubt"
Royal Parade
Eastbourne
E.Sussex BN20 8BB

Contact: Kenneth Fry

Tel: 0232 410300

Voluntary organisation dedicated to supporting charities connected with the sea and furthering public knowledge of British blockade running during the American Civil War. Ships companies learn Victorian seamanship afloat. Free probationary membership by application to secretary. Loan of uniform. Black Powder Club.

Corps of Drums Society and Journal

Stepaside Cottage
The Pudgell, Great Chishill
Royston
Herts SG8 8SE

Contact: Malcolm Hooson

Tel: 0763 838780

The Corps of Drums Society is for any one who plays drum or fife or who believes it is important to keep this traditional music alive. In Britain, the Army takes the lead with a Corps of Drums in every Battalion of Foot Guards, every Regular Battalion of English and Welsh line and in many TA and Cadet Battalions as well. The Society has a photographic library and takes a keen interest in history. Its magazine 'Drummer's Call' is full of interesting illustrations and information. Music meetings are held in London through the year and the Society sponsors occasional musters or concentrations of drums. The Society advises the Army and takes a keen interest in music, training methods and material, instruments and uniform – some of which it supplies. Contact the Hon. Secretary for more details.

Corridors of Time

11 Mulberry Court
Pagham
West Sussex PO21 4TP

Contact: Alan Jeffrey

Tel: 0243 262291
Fax: 0243 262291

Historical promotions and presentations for numerous clients, including English Heritage, National Trust, The Aerospace Museum, TV Production Companies, Walt Disney, Councils and Education Authorities, to name just a few who have benefitted from the extensive expertise of Corridors of Time. Events include multi–period historical spectaculars, town and county shows, and special events plus specialist equestrian input and pyro–technic skills to support other societies. Historical periods include the major eras from Roman to Victorian, including theatre and craft demonstrations and have been seen in Tokyo, USA, Germany, Belgium and Denmark. For an event that makes history!

Croix Du Nord

11 Dunkeld Street
Lanacaster LA1 3DQ

Contact: Neil Harrison

Tel: 0524 35869

Danelaw Dark Age Society

109 Tweendikes Road
Sutton on Hull HU7 4XJ

Contact: Andrew Wiles

Tel: 0482 826617

Dark Ages Society

20 Highwood Close
Shaw
Newbury
Berkshire RG13 2EJ

Contact: Rosanna Day

Tel: 0635 32447 (pm)

Recreation of the late 9th century – the time of Alfred the Great and the Viking invasions. Small, independent group concentrating on accurate recreation of the period, with a balance between warfare and everyday living.

Dawn Fire Folk

112 Hollingworth Road
Lowestoft
Suffolk NR32 4BW

Contact: David Pye

Tel: 0502 83295

Dragons Eye

4 Rosedale Grove
Dormanstown
Redcar
Cleveland

Contact: John Watson

Drayton Bassett Medieval Soc.

10 Drayton Lane
Drayton Bassett
Nr Tamworth
Staffordshire B78 3T2

Contact: Chris Smith

Tel: 0872 285142

Durham 17th Century Society

C/O 24 Tollhouse road
Crossgate Moor
Durham City
Co Durham DH1 4HU

Tel: 0911 3842724

A local branch of the English Civil War Society. Members welcome from both Royalist and Parliamentary factions. Monthly meetings for discussion and mutual assistance at various locations.

Earldom of Wessex

9 Durleigh Close
Headley Park
Bristol
Avon BS13 7NQ

Contact: J.K. Siddorn

Tel: 0272 646818
Fax: 0272 646818

Recreator of the life and times of the peoples of Western England at the turn of the First Millennium. They have resident specialists who research to the highest standards. Battle re–enactments between Vikings, Saxons and Normans complement the 'living history' exhibit, creating living images of those times.

East Anglican Dark Age Society

27 Greenacre Close
Brundall
Norwich NR13 5QF

Contact: John Gibson

Tel: 0603 715649

Eastbourne Men at Arms

11 Sheen Road
Eastbourne
East Sussex

Contact: Barry Harvey

English Companions

38 Granworth Road
Worthing
Sussex BN11 2JF

Contact: Janet Goldsborough

Tel: 0903 207485

Escafeld Medieval Society

94 Langsett Avenue
Sheffield
Sth Yorkshire S6 4AB

Contact: Avril Allott

Tel: 0742 348339

Euro. Union of Historic Re-enactment Groups

169 Southfield Road, Chiswick
London W4 5LB

Contact: Philip Coates–Wright

Aims to encourage contact and cooperation between historic groups internationally.

Euro. Union of Historic Re-enactment Groups

169 Southfield Road, Chiswick
London W4 5LB

Contact: Philip Coates–Wright

Aims to encourage contact and cooperation between historic groups internationally.

Fort Cumberland/Portsmouth Militaria Soc

c/o 49 Lichfield Road
Portsmouth
Hants PO3 6DD

Contact: David Quinton

Tel: 0705 668981

HQ & museum adjacent to Round Tower, Broad Street, Old Portsmouth. Local and military history, postcards & books. Re-enactment group Fort Cumberland Guard Royal Marines 1835-40 period musket & cannon displays. Drum corps have been featured on TV frequently. Free. Mon 7.30pm-9.30pm, Sunday 2.00pm-5.00pm.

Fort Newhaven Military Display Team Ltd.

42 Janes Lane
Burgess Hill
Sussex RH15 0QR

Contact: Richard Hunt

Tel: 0444 233516

A 'living history' society specialising in authentically portraying the British, American and German Forces of the Second World War. Units depicted include: First Airborne Division, Royal Artillery, Royal Sussex Regiment, A.T.S., Military Police, Home Guard and Commando's. Events presented range from battle re-enactments and drill displays to 1940's dances, also displayed are restored military vehicles, artillery and support weapons. The members have assembled much equipment and relevant militaria

over the years and can construct various set pieces from a barrack room inspection scene with kit layouts to a complete British field headquarters. Enthusiastic new members are always welcome.

Garde Imperiale

69 Culverden Park Road
Tunbridge Wells
Kent TN4 9RB

Contact: Dave Paget

Golden Eagle Archery Display Troop

17b St Wilfrids Road
New Barnet
Hertfordshire EN4 9SB

Contact: Roger Summers

Tel: 081 441 7243

Grimwood

21 Cromwell road
Shaw
Newbury
Berkshire

Contact: Paul Blackwall

Tel: 0706 48818

His Britannic Majesty's 95th Reg.

Lowis Place,
112 Hoole Street, Walkley
Sheffield
Sth Yorkshire

Contact: Richard Moore

Tel: 0742 346551

History Re-enactment Workshop

47 Chelmsford Road
South Woodford
London E18 2PW

Contact: Roger Wilson

Tel: 071 930 6727
Fax: 071 505 6463

Histrionix

Tudor Loft
Commonwood House, Commonwood
Kings Langley
Herts WD4 9BA

Contact: Mr D Edge

Infanterie-Regiment

4 Bledlow Cottages
Perry Lane
Bledlow
Bucks

Contact: Howard Giles

Joms Vikings

11a Waddicor Avenue
Ashton-U-Lyne
Lancs OL6 9HE

Contact: Ade Brownlow

Tel: 061 344 1324

Specialising in the Viking and Saxon peoples they provide authentic re-enactment and are available for events throughout the U.K.. Jomsvikings provide main arena battles and Viking village life displays. Video and information pack available. Write for details.

Knights Templar

50 Coppice Road
Marton Grove
Middlesborough
Cleveland

Contact: Jonathan Easby

Knights Templar Medieval Soc.

50 Coppice Road
Marton Grove
Middlesborough
Cleveland

Contact: Jonathan Easby

Knights in Battle Medieval Soc

Brookside Cottage
Franshawe Bank
Dronfield
Sheffield S18 6EY

Contact: Neil Ward

Tel: 0246 411542

Knights of Outremere Medieval Society

39 Chatsworth Road, Clowne
Chesterfield
Derbyshire

Contact: Donna Bell

Tel: 0246 811020

Lewes Reavers

20 Bradford Street
Eastbourne
Sussex BN21 1HC

Tel: 0323 33225

Lincoln Castle Longbowmen

3 Rasen Lane
Lincoln LN1 3DF

Tel: 0522 44936

Mindgames

105a Queen Street
Maidenhead
Berks SL6 1LR

Tel: 0628 770676

Napoleonic Association (42nd Regiment)

25 Stone Court
Stantonbury
Milton Keynes MK14 6AQ

Contact: W Betram

Tel: 0908 320637

National Assoc. Re-enactment Societies

49 Stagsden
Orton Goldhay
Peterborough
Cambs PE2 0RW

Contact: John Crawford

Acts as a forum for historical re-enactment societies in Britain. N.A.R.E.S. provides Codes of Practice relating to safety and authenticity: represents members' interests, including liaison with Government departments and encourages contact between societies and other bodies.

Norse Theatre Co.
4 Ashford Road
Withington
Manchester M20

Contact: Jim Torrence

Tel: 061 434 5620

Norsemen
10 Winfield Avenue
Withington
Manchester 20

Contact: Andy Pettifer

Tel: 061 434 6730

Ordnance Society
12 Farrow Close
Great Moulton
Norwich NR15 2HR

Contact: Rudi Roth

Pheonix WWII Re-enactment Society
19 Kingsood Park Avenue
Peverell
Plymouth
Devon PL3 4NQ

Contact: Rupert Beverley-Smith

Tel: 0752 709203

A re-enactment organisation which portrays WWII German, American and British units of the 1944–5 period. The Society is made up of re-enactors who are military collectors and vehicle enthusiasts who re-enact WWII battles in public and private displays. Members also attend events to put on 'living history' and 'static uniform' displays for the public, visit places of interest, attend various 1940's events, social functions and undertake charity events, particularly for veteran's organisations. Members require fully authentic/original combat uniforms/equipment, weapons and dress uniforms identical to the WWII unit portrayed. Enquiries for membership or bookings for future events are welcomed.

Pike and Shot Society
12 Turner Road
Eaton Ford
St. Neots
Cambridgeshire PE19 3RU

Contact: Christopher Richardson

Tel: 0480 407741

Portsdown Artillery Volunteers
Cliff House
Portsdown Hill, Drayton
Portsmouth
Hampshire PO6 1BS

Contact: Ian Maine

Tel: 0705 327710

Based at Fort Nelson, re-enactment of 1890 Artillery Volunteers. Recreations of drill and specialise in garrison artillery work. Additional activities include demonstrations Martini-Henry Carbine and bayonet drill.

Regia Anglorum
1 Berkley Road
Bedford Place
Southampton
Hampshire

Contact: David Newhouse

Tel: 0703 211053

Ruadin Reivers
Brook Cottage
Cappers Lane
Spurstow
Cheshire CW6 9RP

Contact: Sarah Mawson

Tel: 0829 260131

Sir Richard Hawkswood Company
147 Hadfield Street
Walkley
Sheffield

Contact: John Ansari

Tel: 0742 311071

Sir Thomas Tyldesley's Regiment
C/O 24 Tollhouse road
Crossgate Moor
Durham City
Co Durham DH1 4HV

Contact: The Secretary

Tel: 091 384 2724

A Company of a Royalist Regiment of the English Civil War Society. The Regiment represented was a white coated Royalist Regiment from Lancashire which fought with distinction in the Civil War period and now has a nationwide membership in its recreated form.

Sir William Pennyman's Regiment
70 Hailgate
Howden
Nrth Humberside DN14 7ST

Contact: Jonathan Taylor

Tel: 0430 430695
Fax: 0405 766238

Over 20 years old with 150 members, the group specialises in the re-enactment of the English Civil War and is commited to 'living history'. Families are welcome. Nationwide membership.

Society of the American Revolution
138 Northend Avenue
Portsmouth

Contact: J Harris

Soldier of Fortune
Unit 3a–b Brymau 3 Estate
River Lane, Saltney
Chester CH4 8RQ

Contact: Peter Kabluczenko

Tel: 0244 681090
Fax: 0244 674651

Specialising in U.S. Forces – modern and Vietnam – clothing and equipment. Also stocks British, West and East German, Belgium, Austrian, French and S.W.A.T. equipment, books, replica and deactivated guns, outdoor and survival. 32 page catalogue available at £1.00. Military showroom at Slatney, visit by appointment only. Shops: 56 Lower Bridge St., Chester. 56 Richmond St., Liverpool.

See advertisement in colour section

Southern Skirmish Association Journal
c/o Meadfield Avenue
Langley
Slough
Berks SL3 8HP

Contact: Lawrence Watson

Tel: 0753 810949
Fax: 0753 062828

Founded 1968. American Civil War 'living history' organisation and registered charity specialising in battle re-enactments, 'living history' displays, research and lectures. The Association can also supply museum exhibits. Services include book reviews and advice for media projects. Publishers of 'Skirmisher' a journal of American Civil War articles, published annually and 'Bugle Call' the noticeboard of the Association's activities published every two months. Over 250 events, including those for the Royal Tournament, English Heritage, HMS Warrior, Hertfordshire County Day, Knebworth House, A & M Records and Thames Television have developed experience and expertise. Further details on request.

St. Cuthbert's Land Regia Anglorum
32 Baliol Square
Merryoaks
Durham
Durham DH1 3QH

Contact: Martin Williams

Tel: 091 384 3273

Durham-based, Saxon group of a national re-enactment society. Covers the period 950-1086. Military and civilian activities authentically recreated. Women warriors are welcome. Events held nationally. Regular meetings.

The Carroll County Boys Soc
26 The fleet
Belper
Derbyshire DE5 1NU

Contact: Paul Barrass

Tel: 077382 3513

The Company of Knights
Durendart House
Coles Lane
Capel
Surrey RH5 5HU

Tel: 0306 711141

The Earl of Dumbarton's Foot
98 Suffolk Road
Barking
Essex

Contact: Steve Payne

Tel: 081 594 9958

The English Civil War Society
70 Hailgate
Howden
Nrth Humberside DN14 7ST

Contact: Jonathan Taylor

Tel: 0430 430695
Fax: 0405 766238

The Society, with 2,500 members authentically recreates both the military and civilian aspects of 17th century battles and sieges as well as 'living history' displays and demonstrations of drill.

The Ermine Street Guard
Oakland Farm
Dog Lane
Witcombe
Gloucestershire GL3 4UG

Contact: Chris Haines

Tel: 0452 862235

The society was formed in 1972 to study the Roman army and reconstruct Roman armour and equipment.

The Federation of Dark Age Societies (F.O.D.A.S.)
69 Intwood Road
Norwich NR4 6AA

Contact: Paul Scruton

Tel: 0603 54844

The Free Traders & Revenue Men
91 First Avenue
Gillingham
Kent ME7 2LF

Contact: Mark Dennis

Tel: 0634 54761

The Golden Age Society
19 Madeira Road
Holland-on-Sea
Essex CO15 5HZ

Contact: Chris Dobson

Tel: 0255 813214

The Great War Society 1914-18
316 Westmount Road
Eltham
London SE9 1NL

Contact: Tom Hill

Tel: 0?1 856 8951

The Iron Brigade
161 Waddington Road
Nuneaton
Warwick

Contact: Martin Harbour

Tel: 0203 345886

The Knights of Clifford
65 Millfields Way
Womborne
Staffordshire WV5 8JG

Contact: Ian C Priest

The Knights of Falchion
23 Raby Road
Redcar
Cleveland TS10 2HE

Contact: Barbara Thurston

Tel: 0642 471749

Performs tournament battle re-enactments (both set and free-form) and extensive 'living history' displays including arms, armour and armour production covering the period 1450-1500.

The Knights of Royal England
Camrus House
320 High Street
Sutton
Surrey SM1 1PR

Contact: Jeremy Richardson

Tel: 081 642 9229

The Knights of Theoc
111 Queen's Road
Tewkesbury
Gloucestershire GL20 5EN

Tel: 0684 295921

Medieval entertainment. Hand-to-hand combat, dancing, wrestling, fire eating. 60 miles radius of Tewkesbury only. For information phone after 6.00pm.

The Lion Rampant Medieval Display Society
35 Barnhill Gardens
Marlow
Buckinghamshire SL7 3HB

Contact: Madge Mansfield

Tel: 06284 2372

The Living History Register
21 Oak Road
Woolston
Southampton
Hants SO2 9BQ

Contact: Roger Emmerson

Organisation set-up to educate, inform and communicate through the creation of period environments. The Register also lists volunteers, whom organisers can reach through an annual newsletter.

The Lord General's Staff
17 Gatehead Croft
Delph
Saddleworth
Lancs OL3 5QB

Contact: Rod Lawson

The Medieval Society
90 Crouch House Road
Edenbridge
Kent

Contact: Michael Loades

Tel: 0732 865550

The Napoleonic Association
169 Southfield Road
Chiswick
London W4 5CB

Contact: Philipp Coates-Wright

Tel: 081 994 7220

Furthers interest in the period 1789 to 1815, by research, re-enactment and wargaming. Re-enactment involves battle and 'living history' displays with various Napoleonic regiments portrayed. The research section holds frequent conferences and publishes articles and books. For research queries contact, Paul Chamberlain, 14 Overfield Road, Stopsley, Luton, Beds, LU2 9JU (tel: 0582 24171).

The Norse Film and Pageant Soc
12 Harcourt Drive
Canterbury
Kent CT2 8DP

Contact: Mr M Benstead

The Norse Film & Pageant Soc
Flat 2, 16 Magdala Drive
Mapperley Park
Nottingham NG3 5DF

Contact: Chris Robinson

Tel: 0602 609046

The Queens Lifeguard of Foote
66 Bramble Close
Shrublands, Shirley
Croydon
Surrey

Contact: C Steele

The Regia Anglorum
9 Durleigh Close
Headley Park
Bristol
Avon BS13 7NQ

Contact: J K Siddorn

Tel: 0271 646818
Fax: 0272 646818

An international society, well-known as the principal recreator of the life and times of the folk of these islands in the hundred years preceding the Norman Conquest. They have resident specialists to advise on all aspects of authentic recreation, conducting research to the highest standards. Fully narrated battle re-enactments, often involving around two hundred combatants, create living images of those times. Their tented 'living history' exhibit, the largest and most comprehensive of its kind anywhere, is separately crewed by trained specialist personnel. Also suppliers of props, costume and specialist extras for film and TV.

The Robin Hood Society
37 Moorsham Drive
Wollaton
Nottingham

Contact: Mary Chamberlain

Tel: 0602 285204

The Scottish Horse Museum
The Cross
Dunkeld
Perthshire

The Sealed Knot
3 Fairview Rise
Crich
Matlock
Derbyshire

Contact: Mr P Bentham-Hill

The Second Augusta Roman Re-enactment Society
11 Field Way, Denmead
Portsmouth
Hampshire PO7 6EQ

Contact: Richardson

The Seventeenth Century Heritage Cntr
3 Penley Avenue
Prestatyn
Clwyd

Contact: John Carter

The Society of the American Revolution
8 Warren Court
Underdown Road
Southwick
Sussex BN42 4HN

Contact: George Bailey

'Living history' group specialising in the period 1775-1782. Wide variety of national and international activities covering all aspects of the hobby. Send s.a.e for further information.

The Southern Skirmish Assoc
Wycke Lane
Tollesbury
Essex CM9 8ST

Contact: Tom Brown

The Sword and the Scimitar Medieval Society
Flat 2, Ayleswade Court
East Harnham
Salisbury SP2 8DS

Contact: D Canham

Val Winship's Medieval Jousting Tournament,
The Lazy 'W', Yapton Lane
Walberton
West Sussex BN18 0AS

Contact: Val Winship

Tel: 0243 551405

Valhalla Vikings
12 Kersley Street
Battersea
London SW11 4PT

Contact: Jane Malcolm-Davies

Tel: 071 350 2378

Viking Hammer of the West
Plas Berw
Gaerwen
Anglesey LL60 6HY

Contact: Orm Skoffin

Tel: 024 877 878

WWII Battle Re-enactment Assoc Ltd.
c/o 280 Silverdale Road
Reading
Berks RG6 2NU

Tel: 0734 351381

The World War II Batle Re-enactment Association Ltd. is one of the largest WWII re-enactment groups in Europe. It holds events throughout the country, usually every two months, with extra shows in the summer. There are also social events and trips to battlefields. The aim of WWIIBRA is to try to understand what life was like as a British, American or German WWII combat soldier, experiencing the excitement and comradeship of front line life. A high standard of authenticity is maintained. The £15 subscription fee entitles members to attend events free, and additionally to a two-monthly newletter packed with information.

Wessex Dark Age Society
1 Castle Hill Cottages
Abbotsbury Beach
Weymouth
Dorset DT3 4LA

Contact: Barry Hennesey

Tel: 0303 871489

Westbury-on-Trym Saxon Society
45 Lakewood Crescent
Henleaze
Bristol BS10 5HL

Contact: R Glover

Wargames Groups and Suppliers

AGEMA
6 Studley Road
Linthorpe
Middlesborough
Cleveland

Contact: I. Moran

Bath Wargames Club
16 The Penns
Clevedon
Avon BS21 5AN

Tel: 0272 876856

Birmingham Wargames Society
5c Calthorpe Mansions
Calthorpe Road
Birmingham B15 1QS

Contact: Martin Healey

Tel: 021 454 1058

Bunshop A
52 Meadow Walk
Ewell
Surrey KT17 2ED

Contact: M. Klaka

Central London Wargamers
23 Rothay
Albany Street
London NW1 4DH

Contact: S. Sola

Chichester Wargames Society
7 Bellemeade Close
Woodgate
Chichester
West Sussex PO20 6YD

Contact: Andy Gilbert

Tel: 0243 544339

Meets Tuesday evenings and once a month for a whole day. All periods covered, but specialise in 15mm Ancients, naval wargaming, 5mm Napoleonic and ECW. Regular entrants in national competitions and World Wargaming Championships.

Clarke, S.
4 Derfel Cottages
London Road
Frodsham
Cheshire WA6 7DS

Contact: Clarke, S.

Colchester Wargames Association
10 Golden Noble Hill
Colchester
Essex

Contact: Pete Anglish

Tel: 0206 563190

Most periods and scales covered. Meets weekly.

Cornwall Wargames Society
Women's Institute Hall
Cranstock Street
Newquay
Cornwall

Tel: 0209 212357

All periods catered for including fantasy. Membership fees per annum, £10.00 seniors, £5.00 juniors, £5.00 associated. £1.00 table fee per person per game. Meetings bi–monthly.

Devizes & District Wargamers
15 Chiltern Close
Warminster
Wiltshire BA12 8QU

Durham Wargames Group
c/o Gilesgate Community Assoc
Vane Tempest Hall, Gilesgate
Durham City
Co Durham

Tel: 091 3847659

One of the longest established groups in the area now in its 23rd year. Annual conventions. All periods and scales including some SF and Fantasy. Weekly meetings.

Eagle Miniatures
Wild Acre
Minchinhampton
Glos GL6 9AJ

Contact: David Atkins

Tel: 0453 835782

Design, manufacture and distribute 15mm, 25mm and 54mm figures from the Seven Years, Napoleonic and American Civil War. A 'design and cast' service is available. Call by appointment. Occasionally hosts megagames.

East Leeds Militaria Society
Crossgates Bowling Club
Well Garth, Off Station Road
Leeds 15

Forlorn Hope
9 Brocklehurst Street
New Cross
London SE14 5QG

Contact: C. Barrass

Tel: 071 639 3240

Gorby's Boysteam
7 Heathfield Close
Upper Weston
Bath BA1 4NW

Contact: S. Chasey

Green, A.
3 Merston Place
Evesham
Worcs WR11 4AZ

Contact: Green, A.

Halifax Wargames Society
7 Brookeville Avenue
Hipperholme
Halifax
Yorks HX3 8DZ

Contact: Roger Greenwood

Tel: 0422 203169

Open to players of all wargaming periods and game styles. Weekly meetings. Contact secretary for details of Ragnar Brothers Games a wargames group interesting in developing wargames rules and boardgames.

Harrogate Wargamers Club
22 St John's Road
Bilton
Harrogate
West Yorkshire HG1 3AF

Contact: Ian Garbutt

Organises the annual SABRE wargames show. Weekly meetings.

Harrogate & Solo Wargamers Soc
11 Lancaster Drive
Clayton–Le–Moors
Accrington
Lancs BB5 5RD

IND
9 Camp View Road
St Albans
Herts

Contact: M. Scales

Inidv MK C Members
13 Spring Drive
Stevenage
Herts

Contact: B. Mills

Jackson, C.
2 Gagewell Drive
Horbury
Wakefield
W. Yorks WF4 6BP

Contact: Jackson, C.

Tel: 0924 271305

Kirriemuir & Dis Wargames Soc
Glengate Hall
Glengate Hall
Kirriemuir
Tayside
Scotland

Contact: Dale Smith

Tel: 0575 74128

Mac's Models
133–135 Canongate
Royal Mile
Edingburgh EH8 8BP

Tel: 031 557 5551

Mailed Fist Wargames Group
Hyde Festival Theatre
Corporation Street
Hyde
Chesire

Maltby and Dis. Wargamers Soc
Church Hall, School Lane
Maltby
Rotherham

Tel: 0709 477977

Malvern Wargames Club
37 Court Road
Malvern

Contact: Dave Bolton

Tel: 0684 560383

Manchester Board Wargames
St. Chad's Church Hall
Guywood Lane
Romily, Nr Stockport M20 9DU

Contact: Norman Lane

Tel: 061 494 2604

Bi–monthly meetings. Main interests are historical board wargames including Squad Leader, Republic of Rome, SPI games and general games. Lending library of games and magazines.

Manx Military Modelling Society
62 Port–E–Chee Avenue
Douglas
Isle of Man

Contact: David Sharpe

Tel: 0624 676084

Society formed to promote both large scale military modelling and historical based wargaming. Adult subscription £7.00, no age restrictions.

McBriar, D.
9 Talisman Close
Runcorn
Cheshire WA7 6JS

Contact: McBriar, D.

Tel: 0928 312729

Methusalens
5 Fairfax Avenue
Oxford
Oxon OX3 0RP

Contact: M. Goddard

Norway Blues
23 Cherrywood Avenue
Englefield
Egham
Surrey TW2 0TE

Contact: C. Smith

Oxford A
316 Thorney Leys
Witney
Oxon OX8 7YP

Contact: D. Fairhurst

Tel: 0993 771398

Plato Rep
35 Whyteladies Lane
Cookham
Berks

Contact: C. Robinson

Rawdons Routers
5 Shiplate Road
Bleadon Village
Weston Super Mare BS24 0NG

Contact: D. Aynsley

Red October
19 Plants Brook Road
Walmley
Sutton Coldfield
West Midlands B76 8EX

Contact: R. Boyles

Tel: 021 313 1053

Reigate Wargames Group
The White Cottage
8 Westhill Avenue
Epsom
Surrey KT19 8LE

Contact: Ian McNeil

Tel: 03727 21070

Areas of interest are Naopoleonics and Ancients, W.W.II, A.C.W. and board games. Meet at Redlands Centre, Croydon Road, Reigate weekly and bi-monthly. Contact club secretary for further details.

Society of Ancients
12 Turner Road
Eaton Ford
St. Neots
Cambridgeshire PE19 3RU

Contact: Christopher Richardson

Tel: 0480 407741

Solo Wargamers Association
63 Beckingham Road
Guildford
Surrey GU2 6BT

South East Essex Military Society
202 Westcliff Park Drive
Westcliff–On–Sea
Essex SS0 9LR

Contact: John Francis

Tel: 0702 431878

Historical wargaming with all periods covered. Produces major demonstration game each year and runs annual wargames show 'Present Arms'. Meets weekly.

South East London Wargames Grp
16 West Hallowes
Eltham
London SE9 4EX

Contact: Paul Greenwood

Tel: 081 857 6107

The South East London Wargames Group (known as SELWG) was formed in 1971 and has a membership of over 100. A wide range of interests are catered for in the wargaming field. The club also runs an annual open day.

See advertisement facing contents page

Stockton Wargamers
c/o Elmwood Community Centre
Green lane, Hartburn
Stockton on Tees

Contact: Garry Harbottle–Johnson

Tel: 0642 580019

All periods (also includes Ancient, Science Fiction and Fantasy). Played in all scales and formats; tabletop, board games, role playing. Frequent 'in club' campaigns and day trips to conventions, painball, LRP etc. Annual weekend camping trip. Miniumum age 12. Annual membership £2.00.. Annual show.

Stormin Normans
26 South Norwood Hill
London SE25 6AB

Contact: N. Scott

Stourbridge District Wargamers
72 Severn Road
Halesowen
West Midlands B63 2NL

Contact: Ashley Hewitt

Tel: 0384 61389

Weekly meetings. Membership fee dependent on age. Most periods catered for with role–playing and board games.

S.E. Scotland Wargames Club
182 Easter Road
Edinburgh EH7 5QQ

The French Horn
Oxford Road
Gerrards Close
Bucks SL9 7DP

Contact: G. Fordham

The Good, Bad, Ugly
47 Norwich Road
Thornton Heath
Surrey CR4 8NA

Contact: G. Woodhead

Tel: 081 653 2873

The Napoleonic Association
169 Southfield Road
Chiswick
London W4 5CB

Contact: Philipp Coates-Wright

Tel: 081 994 7220

Furthers interest in the period 1789 to 1815, by research, re-enactment and wargaming. Re-enactment involves battle and 'living history' displays with various Napoleonic regiments portrayed. The research section holds frequent conferences and publishes articles and books. For research queries contact, Paul Chamberlain, 14 Overfield Road, Stopsley, Luton, Beds, LU2 9JU (tel: 0582 24171).

The Regiment
The Baildon Craft Centre
Browgate
Baildon
West Yorkshire

Tel: 0274 547671

The South Dorset Military Soc
23 Monks Way
Bearwood
Bournemouth
Dorset BH11 9HT

Contact: B Thorburn

Tel: 0202 576423

The Timelords
26 Latin Close
Offord Cluny
Huntingdon
Cambs PE18 9RL

Contact: C. Jackson

Tel: 0480 810997

Ulster Freikorps A
32 Kilmakee Park
Gilnahirk
Belfast BT5 7QY

Contact: S. Sandford

Tel: 0232 797766

Ulster Freikorps Levy
16 Marmont Park
Belfast BT4 2GR

Contact: D. Taylor

Tel: 0232 760581

Ulster Military Modelling Society
35 Kilmakee Park
Belfast BT5 7QY

Contact: Jeremy Dowd

The society specialises in wargaming, catering for most periods and scales, running multi-player games, campaigns and competitions. Organises the Ulster Militaria each year. Meets monthly at Creagagh Library. Write for details.

U.N.I.T.S. Wargames Services
40 Cranbrook Street
Barnsley
South Yorks S70 6LP

Tel: 0226 295180

Virgin Soldiers
75 Woodford Green Road
Hall Green
Birmingham

Contact: M. McVeigh

Tel: 021 778 5582

Weston Scorpions
5 Shiplate Road
Bleadon Village
Weston Super Mare BS24 0NG

Contact: R. Aynsley

Wild Geese II
27 Kingsdale Croft
Stretton
Burton on Trent

Contact: D. McHugh

Wargame Equipment

Battlements
The Old Anchor of Hope
Lammas
Norwich
Norfolk NR10 5AF

Contact: Ian Weekly

Tel: 0603 279708

Known for high-quality 'one-off' model buildings in all scales for wargamers, display and museums.

Bello Wargames Figures & Accessories
88 Deerswood Court
Ifield
Crawley
West Sussex RH11 0HF

Tel: 0293 549449

Manufacturers of wargame figures in 1:200 scale (9/10mm). Range cover periods from Ancient Greeks to World War I. Send s.a.e. for free catalogue and sample figure.

Britannia Miniatures
33 St. Mary's Road
Halton Village
Runcorn
Cheshire WA7 2BJ

Contact: David Howitt

Tel: 0928 564906

25mm wargame figures, Ancients, Colonial, Napoleonic, Crimea, Pony Wars etc. 20mm Great War, early period Germans, British and equipment. Expanding range of wargame accessories cast in resin.

Mail order only. Callers by appointment. Non-illustrated listings available. Large s.a.e. required.

Chart Hobby Distributors Ltd
Chart House, Station Road
East Preston
Littlehampton
West Sussex BN16 3AG

Tel: 0903 773170

UK importers and distributors of Avalon Hill and Victory Games Inc. Publishers of military simulation games, Fasa Corporation and Sci-fi games Battletech, Renegade Legion and Shadowrun. Also other games from Columbia, 3W's and Mayfair. Distributed in hobby and games stores nationally.

Connoisseur Figures
20a Coastal Road
Burniston
Scarborough
North Yorks YO13 0HR

Contact: Chris Gilder

Tel: 0723 870741
Fax: 0723 870741

Specialists in 25mm figures. Full mail order catalogue available with all their ranges, Napoleonic, Colonial, Pony Wars, American Civil War, Renaissance etc. 20% discount on all figures bought from their shop.

Dean Forest Figures
62 Grove Road
Berry Hill
Coleford
Glos GL16 8QX

Contact: Phillip Beveridge

Tel: 0594 36130

Wargame figures painted to three standards. 15mm, 20mm or 25mm scales. Trees, buildings and terrain features made to order. All hand built, painted and highly detailed. Also large scale figures 54mm and UP painted. One-off large scale figures made to order.

D. Hewins Models & Hobbies
7 East St. Mary's Gate
Grimsby
South Humberside DN31 1LH

Tel: 0472 347088

Stockists of 'Men at Arms' and many other military books and magazines. All makes of plastic kits. Wargaming and fantasy figures, plus other relevant items. General modelling and scenery accessories. Military and fantasy board/role playing games. Open Mon-Wed Fri-Sat, 9.00am-5.30pm.

Eagle Software & First Empire Software
6 Cranmore Drive
Highley
Bridgnorth
Shropshire WV16 6DS

Contact: David Watkins

Tel: 0746 862455

Publishers of Napoleonic computer moderated tabletop wargaming simulation 'Follow the Eagle V', various machine specifications available. Also publishers of the only dedicated Napoleonic gaming magazine, 'First Empire', published monthly. Mail order and trade supplied.

Elite Miniatures
26 Bowlease Gardens
Bessacarr
Doncaster
South Yorks DN4 6AP

Contact: Peter Morbey

Tel: 0302 530038

A range of high quality 25mm metal figures for the wargamer and collector. The range covers the Napoleonic Wars, Seven years War and Punic Wars. For details of a consistantly expanding range please send a s.a.e. for the latest catalogue or see their advertisments in Wargames Illustrated Magazine. This range of figures is available by direct mail order from the U.K. or for their U.S. customers from Elite Miniatures U.S.A., 2625 Forest Glen Trail, Riverwoods, Ill. 60015, USA.

Essex Miniatures
Unit 1, Shannon Centre
Shannon Square
Canvey Island
Essex SS8 9UD

Tel: 0268 682309
Fax: 0268 510151

Manufacturer of 15mm & 25mm metal figures. Send s.a.e. for catalogue. Figures supplied by mail order. All major credit cards accepted.

FJ Associates
60 Frederica Road
Winton
Bournemouth
Dorset BH9 2NA

Tel: 0202 511495

Company dealing in wargame insurance.

Frei-Korps 15
25 Princetown Road
Bangor
Co. Down BT20 3TA

Contact: Cameron Robinson

Tel: 0247 472860

Large range of 15mm scale wargame figures. Publisher of a series of military campaign books and rules. Periods covered included Ancient, Thirty Years War, Seven Years War, American Wars 1774-1880's, British in India, Europe 1850-1870 and artillery.

Hinchcliffe Models

28 Brook Street
Wymeswold
Loughborough
Leics LE12 6TU

Wargame figure manufacturer producing range of 25mm figures covering Ancient, Dark Ages, Renaissance, Seven Years War, English Civil War, American War of Independence, Napoleonic, A.C.W. and Colonial periods. Also artillery and associated equipment and white metal WWII vehicle model kits. All retailed through Skytrex Ltd..

Kernow Miniatures

44 Bawden Road
Bodmin
Cornwall PL31 1PU

Contact: Jon Meech

Tel: 0208 75898

Full-time painting service for all wargaming needs. All popular scales undertaken to a choice of wargame or collector standards. Send for samples and price guide.

Lancashire Games (Mail Order)

20 Platting Road
Lydgate
Oldham
Lancs OL4 4DL

Contact: Allan Lumley

Tel: 0497 872212

Offers a range of miniatures from Renaissance to Colonial in 15mm, main ranges are horse and musket periods (Seven Years War to American Civil War). Painting service available on own range of miniatures and most other popular manufacturers. Send s.a.e. for full lists.

Leisure Games

91 Ballard's Lane
Finchley
London N3 1XY

Tel: 081 346 2327

Comprehensive range of brand war games, wargames rules, 'Men at Arms' reference books and minifigures. Mail order service. Send s.a.e. for list. Shop open Mon–Fri 9.30am–6.00pm, Sat 9.00am–5.30am.

Long Range Logistics

41 Whorlton Road
Stockton on Tees
Cleveland TS19 8NH

Contact: Garry Harbottle–Johnson

Tel: 0642 670107

Mail order and wargames show trader. Specialist in 20th century 6mm models, also 6mm science fiction, rules and scenics for all periods (ancient – science fiction) in all scales. Rules and army list authors/publishers and specialist stockist of 6mm aircraft. Callers by appointment only.

Matchlock Miniatures

26 Cliffsea Grove
Leigh-on-Sea
Essex SS9 1NQ

Contact: David Ryan

Tel: 0702 73986

Produce wargames figures of the highest historical accuracy. Scales from 10mm to 25, periods from Ancient to the Korean War; specialising in the C17th and C18th. Mail order.

Model Figures & Hobbies

4 Lower Balloo Road
Groomsport
Co. Down BT19 2LU

Contact: Norman Robinson

Tel: 0247 883187

Manufacturer of Platoon 20 WWII and modern wargame figures and equipment. Also Ensign 1/1200 scale model ships and aircraft and the Plastiform scenics range of Vacforms.

Museum Miniatures

17 Hilderthorpe Road
Bridlington
Yorks YO15 3AY

Contact: Dave Hoyles

Tel: 0262 670421

15mm and 25mm wargaming figures cast in English pewter, for maximum definition and environmentally safe (no lead). Ranges include, Ancient, Dark Ages, Medieval, Renaissance, A.C.W., Napoleonic. Equipment includes wagons, carts, cannons, bombards, catapults. Mail order service a speciality with a 7 day turn round. Callers welcome but are advised to ring first.

Navwar

11 Electric Parade
Seven Kings Road
Ilford
Essex IG3 8BY

Contact: William McKenzie

Tel: 081 590 6731
Fax: 081 590 6731

Manufacturers of 1/1200th and 1/3000th ships, Naismith Design, Roundway Miniatures and Heroics and Ros Figures, Publishers. Complete selection of Osprey, wargame rules, paint and action zoo. Mail order specialists. Trade enquiries welcome. Open Mon–Sat (except Thurs), 9.00am–5.30pm.

Robinson Imports

25 Princetown Road
Bangor
Co. Down BT20 3TA

Contact: Cameron Robinson

Tel: 0247 472860

Importer of Italian model figure range Mirliton S.G. 25mm, Ancient, Medieval, Renaissance, French Revolutionary, Napoleonic Wars, Italian War of Independence 1859. Also available 'Empire, Eagles & Lions' Napoleonic wargames magazine.

Skytrex Ltd.

Unit 3
Canal Bank
Loughborough
Leics LE11 0HF

Tel: 0509 213789
Fax: 0509 230874

Manufacturer and retailer of wargame models. Stock includes Davco, Tritorn, Hincliffe and Firefight. All ranges available by mail order. Factory shop 9.00am–4.00pm or specialist retail shops.

Spielfreaks

P.O. Box 30
Thetford
Norfolk IP25 6UZ

Contact: Eamon Bloomfield

Stockists of used games and magazines. Send s.a.e. for listing.

Tabletop Games

53 Mansfield Road
Daybrook
Nottingham
Notts NG5 6BB

Contact: Robert Connor

Tel: 0602 205484

Suppliers for wargamers for 15 years TTG specialise in a fast mail order service anywhere in the world. Publishers of own rules and manufacturers of figures they also supply other manufacturers products. Send s.a.e. for free mail order catalogue.

Terence Wise Military Books
Pantiles
Garth Lane
Knighton
Powys LD7 1HH

Contact: Terence Wise

Specialists in the supply of Regimental and Divisional histories, mostly Britain and Commonwealth, but also for the armies of all major countries. Free catalogues spring and autumn listing over 1,000 titles. The company also publishes reprints of rare military titles, a guide to military museums and rules and titles for wargamers.

The Drum
107 Watling Street West
Towcester
Northants NN12 7AG

Contact: Michael Green

Tel: 0327 359276
Fax: 0327 50435

Stockists of wargames figures and boardgames, fantasy & sci-fi roleplaying games and mail order service. Manufacturers of resin buildings and accessories for the wargaming and role playing hobbies. Open Mon–Thur 9.30am–5.30pm, Fri & Sat 9.30am–6.00pm. Send s.a.e. for resin castings catalogue.

The Iron Duke
Edgehill Cottage
Ropeyard
Wotton Bassett
Wilts SN4 7BW

Contact: Ian Barstow

Tel: 0793 850805

Professional wargames figure painter and dealer in second hand painted figures and armies. All scales. Guaranteed no sub-contracting. All major credit cards.

The Miniature Architect
23 Wylam Street
Craghead
Stanley
Co. Durham DH9 6ER

Contact: Andrew Copestake

Tel: 0207 283332

Maker of high quality handbuilt model buildings and fortification in all scales from 1/300–1/32 for the discerning collector, or wargamer. May be purchased from their "off the peg" list or specially commissioned to customer requirements. From single models to cities, from log cabins to castles, dioramas and landscapes also constructed and painted to customer specification in any scale 1/300–1/32. Write with s.a.e. or 2 IRC stating interests or requirements. Personal callers by prior arrangement only.

Vandrad
7 Marpool Hill
Exmouth
Devon EX8 2LJ

Contact: Rick Lawrence

Tel: 0395 278664

Importers of RSM Miniatures and quality wargames figures: 20mm Napoleonic, ACW, Colonial; 25mm SYW, AWI, plus 18th century uniform guides and rules; U.S. and Battle for Empire rules. Also stocks 'Historical Gamer' the U.S. wargames magazine, Rank & File 1859, 1866, 1970–71 15mm figures. Send 3 x 1st class stamps for catalogue.

Wargames Foundry
The Foundry
Mount Street
New Basford
Notts NG7 7HX

Tel: 0602 792002
Fax: 0602 792209

Wargames Research Group
The Keep, Le Marchant Barracks
London Road
Devizes
Wilts SN10 2ER

Warpaint Figure Painting
20 Swaledale Crescent
Barnwell
Houghton-le-Spring
Tyne and Wear DH4 7NT

Tel: 091 385 7070

Warrior Miniatures
14 Tiverton Avenue
Glasgow G32 9NX

Contact: John Holt

Tel: 041 778 3426

Manufacturer of wargaming figures: 15mm, 25mm etc. Send for full catalogue & price list s.a.e. + £1.25. State interests for sample. Mail order only. Visa, Access. Ranges include 15mm Colonials, Napoleonics, Fantasy, ACW, ECW. 25mm Napoleonics, Samurai, Dark Ages, Ancients, Medievals. 20mm Modern, Spanish Civil War. 24 hour answerphone.

Wessex Rules
42 Danecroft Road
Herne Hill
London SE24 9NZ

Contact: Colin Stutt

Tel: 071 274 0732

Producers of rules for 15 and 25mm wargames. Ancient rules cost £7.50 plus 75p postage U.K., £1.50 foreign.

Publishers

Acme Publishing Co.
Holmsdale Road
South Darenth Kent
DA4 9AF

After The Battle
Church House
Church Street
London E15 3JA

Tel: 081 534 8833
Fax: 081 555 7567

Publisher of books and magazines that specialise in revisiting the battlefields of World War II and presenting stories through 'then and now' photographic comparisons. 'Wheels and Tracks' magazine covers the history, use, restoration and preservation of

military vehicles.

Airlife Publishing
101, Longden Road
Shrewsbury
Shropshire SY3 9EB

Tel: 0743 235651
Fax: 0743 232944

Publishes books on all aspects of aeronautics with particular emphasis on contemporary and historical military aviation. Also represents in Europe, the aviation and military titles of Tab–Aero Inc. and the list of the U.S. Naval Institute Press. Free catalogues available on request.

Alan Sutton Publishing
Pheonix Mill
Far Thrupp
Stroud
Gloucestershire GL5 2BU

Contact: Tessa Webb

Tel: 0453 731114
Fax: 0453 731117

Non-fiction, history based publisher. List features many illustrated military titles including the following:
British Butchers and Bunglers of WWI
£14.95
Damn the Dardanelles!
£14.95
On the Western Front
£7.95 (pb)
The Western Front Illustrated
£16.99
World War I in Postcards
John Laffin £14.95 £7.95 (pb)
1100 Miles with Monty
Norman Kirby £12.95

The Boar War in Old Postcards
Ian McDonald £14.95
From Arctic Snow to Dust of Normandy
Patrick Dalzel–Job £14.95
The German Occupation of the Channel Islands
Charles Cruickshank £15.95
The Island of Dread
Brian Bonnard £14.99
Mander's March on Rome
Col. d'A Mander £10.95
Marlborough Revisited and the War Remembered
M. Wharton £5.95 (pb)
The Road to Waterloo
Alan Guy £16.99
A Strange War: Burma Indian and Afghanistan
£12.95
1914–1919
Chris Mills
From All Sides
Bob Willey £4.95 (pb)
Available from all good bookshops or direct from the above address. Catalogue and stocklist available on request.

Andre Deutsch Ltd.
105–106 Great Russell Street London WC1B 3LJ

Tel: 071 580 2746
Fax: 071 631 3253

Anschluss Publishing
"Rivendell"
Wathen Way, Marsham
Aylsham
Norfolk NR10 5PZ

Argus Books
Eddington Hook Ltd.
406 Vale Road
Tonbridge
Kent TN9 1XR

Arms and Armour Press, Cassell PLC
Villiers House
41–47 Strand
London WC2N 5JE

Contact: Roderick Dymott

Tel: 071 839 4900
Fax: 071 839 1804

Established for 25 years Arms & Armour Press have a military publishing list producing over 50 titles each year covering aviation, land warfare, naval action and ships, fire arms and topics relevant to collectors, modellers and outdoorsmen.

Arrow Books Ltd.
Brookmount House
62–65 Chandos Place
London WC2N 4NW

Tel: 071 240 3411
Fax: 071 836 1409

Ashton Arts
15 Love Lane
Cirencester
Gloucestershire GL7 1YG

Aston Publications
10 Christchurch Road
London N8 9QL

Athena Books
34 Imperial Crescent
Town Moor
Doncaster
South Yorkshire DN2 5BU

Tel: 0302 322913
Fax: 0302 730531

Large stockist of military history from 3000BC to WW3. Also specialist sections on Wild West and American Civil War. Over 50,000 new and out–of–print books available. Send for free list. Open Mon–Sat, 9.15am–4.45pm.

BT Batsford
4 Fitzhardinge Street
London W1H 0AH

Barrie & Jenkins Ltd.
289 Westbourne Grove
London W11 2QA

Tel: 071 229 9636
Fax: 071 229 4571

Beaufort Publishing Ltd.
PO Box 22
Liphook
Hants GU30 7PJ

Tel: 042 876 588

Specialist publishers producing books on castles. The company publish the highly illustrated quarterly journal 'Fortress' (subscription £18 UK, £20 overseas) and a range of new and reprinted books. They also offers a mail-order list of over 120 books on every aspect of the subject, from hillforts to the Atlantic Wall, including imported, foreign–language and hard to find titles. Send for a free 'Fortress' brochure or booklist.

Belmont Publishing
10 White Horse Street
London W1Y 7LB

Berg Publishers Ltd.
150 Cowles Road
Oxford
Oxon OX4 1JJ

Contact: Marion Berghaan

Tel: 0865 245 104
Fax: 0865 791165

Academic publisher with a strong list in European – especially German – military studies.

Bertram Rota Ltd.
9–11 Langley Court
London WC2E 9RX

Blackwell Publishers
108 Cowley Road
Oxford OX4 1JF

Tel: 0865 791100
Fax: 0865 791347

Academic publisher with some military history titles including civil war and World War I. Information sheets and current titles available.

Bloomsbury Press
2 Soho Square
London W1V 5DE

Tel: 071 494 2111

Book Club Associates
87 Newman Street
London W1P 4EN

Tel: 071 637 0341
Fax: 071 631 3762

Book club offering selected discounted books in the following subject areas: Modern, World War II, World War I, Colonial, American Civil War, Napoleonic, Horse and Musket, Medieval and Ancient Warfare, Aviation, Weapons, Modelling, Wargaming, Naval and Uniforms. After a special bargain starting offer, members commit to buy four books in the first year of membership. Books are offered with at least 20% discount. Monthly Bulletin gives details of approx. 200 new titles per year.

Boydell & Brewer Ltd.
PO Box 9
Woodbridge
Suffolk IP12 3DF

Tel: 0394 411320

Specialist in medieval history from 600–1500: King Arthur, knighthood, castles, warfare, armour, fine arts etc. Send s.a.e. for catalogue.

Brassey's Defence Publishers
Headington Hill Hall
Oxford OX3 0BW

Breedon Books
45 Friar Gate
Derby DE1 1DA

Broadsword Publishing
6 Cranleigh Gardens
Sanderstead
South Croydon CR2 9LD

Cambridge University Press
The Edinburgh Building
Shaftesbury Road
Cambridge CB2 2RU

Tel: 0223 312393

Central Books
14 The Leathermarket
London SE1 3ER

Tel: 071 407 5447

Centre for Security & Conflict Studies
12a Golden Square
London W1R 3AF

Tel: 071 439 7381

Cheshire Volunteer
2 Brookside Road
Fordsham
Cheshire WA6 7BL

Tel: 051 495 1254

Collectors' Books Ltd.
Bradley Lodge
Kemble
Cirencester
Gloucestershire GL7 6AD

Contact: Christian Braun

Tel: 0285 770 239
Fax: 0285 770 896

Publishers of 'The Little Ships of Dunkirk' and of 'Bluebird' – both describing the privately owned pleasure cruises that took part in the Dunkirk rescue.

Collins Publishers
Ophelia House
Fulham Palace Road
London W6

Tel: 081 741 7070

Conway Maritime Press
24 Bride Lane
Fleet Street
London EC4Y 8DR

Crecy Books
The Triangle
Somerton
Somerset TA11 6QJ

Tel: 0272 835835

Datafile Books
10 White Hart Lane
Wistaston
Crewe
Cheshire CW2 8EX

Contact: Malcolm Bellis

Tel: 0270 663296

David & Charles Publishers plc
Brunel House
Newton Abbot
Devon TQ12 4PU

Tel: 0626 61121
Fax: 0626 67047

Edwards, Francis
The Old Cinema
Castle Street
Hay-on-Wye
Hereford HR3 5DF

Tel: 0497 820071
Fax: 0497 821004 F

Facts on File
Collins Street
Oxford OX4 1XJ

Tel: 0865 728399

Fieldbooks
24 Callendar Close
St Nicolas' Park
Nuneaton
Warks CV11 6LV

Contact: Paddy Griffith

Tel: 0203 350763

Also incorporating Paddy Griffith Associates, the company publishes a range of military books.

Firebird Books Ltd.
PO Box 327
Poole
Dorset BH15 2RG

Tel: 0202 715349
Fax: 0202 736191

Publishers of illustrated military history books including the 'Heroes and Warriors' series. Free illustrated catalogue on request. Mail order.

Forman, Adrian
13 Shepherd Market
Mayfair
London W1Y 8LA

Tel: 071 429 6599

Fort Cumberland/Portsmouth Militaria Soc
c/o 49 Lichfield Road
Portsmouth
Hants PO3 6DD

Contact: David Quinton

Tel: 0705 668981

HQ & museum adjacent to Round Tower, Broad Street, Old Portsmouth. Local and military history, postcards & books. Re-enactment group Fort Cumberland Guard Royal Marines 1835–40 period musket & cannon displays. Drum corps have been featured on TV frequently. Free. Mon 7.30pm–9.30pm, Sunday 2.00pm–5.00pm.

Galago Publishing Ltd.
Bromley Shopping Hall
16–20 Widmore Road
Bromley
Kent 1BR1 1RY

Contact: T. Stiff

Tel: 081 290 0245

Goodall Publications Ltd.
Larchwood House
274 London Road
St Albans
Hertfordshire AL1 1HY

Tel: 0727 61611

Greenhill Books
Park House
1 Russell Gardens
London NW11 9NN

Tel: 081 458 6314
Fax: 081 905 5245

Publisher of books on military history. Their Napoleonic library has, at the time of writing, twenty volumes and they have reprinted classic books by Sir Charles Oman. Books on Special Forces (SAS, SBS, SEALs). Write for illustrated catalogue.

HMSO Books
St Crispins
Duke Street
Norwich NR3 1PD

Tel: 0603 622211
Fax: 0603 7582

Harrap Ltd.
19–23 Ludgate Hill
London EC4M 7PD

Tel: 071 248 6444
Fax: 071 248 3357

History Books/Military Books
2 The Broadway
London N11 3DU

Tel: 081 368 8568
Fax: 081 368 8568

Specialist in military history. Large stock of new and second hand books including many imported titles, on uniforms, weapons, unit histories, biographies, battles, campaigns, espionage and terrorism. Annotated catalogues issued each of over 1000

titles, which often includes videos and computer simulations.

1. General military.

2. American military achievement. From the Revolution to the Gulf.

3. German and European Axis World War II Armed Forces.

£1.00 per catalogue. Visa and Mastercard accepted. Visitors welcome between 10.00am–1.00pm Tues to Fri inclusive. The hours are different at Christmas and other public holidays, it is always advisable to telephone prior to calling.

H.B.T.
67c Port Street
Stirling FK8 2ER
Scotland

Tel: 0786 78979

ISO Publications
137 Westminster Bridge Road
London SE1

Ian Allan Ltd.
Terminal House
Shepperton
Middlesex TW17 8AS

Tel: 0932 228950

Publishers of military, aviation and transport subjects, including the 'Collectors Guide, 'At War' and 'ABC' series along with the monthly magazine 'Raids'. Also runs specialist interest bookshops in London and Birmingham and a mail order service through Bookpoint (39 Milton Park, Abingdon, OX14 4TD).

International Military Books
76 Priestfield Road
Gillingham
Kent ME7 4RF

Tel: 0634 574387

Internat. Inst. for Strategic Studies
23 Tavistock Street
London WC2E 7NQ

Tel: 071 379 7676

I.B. Tauris & Co Ltd.
3 Henrietta Street
London WC2E 8PW

Tel: 071 836 5814

Jane's Publishing Co Ltd.
238 City Road
London EC1V 2PU

Tel: 071 251 9281
Fax: 071 251 8900

Johnston, A.A.

Pitney

Langport

Somerset

Tel: 0458 72713

Landmark Booksellers
6 Lime Grove
Westfield
Woking
Surrey GU22 9PW

Tel: 0483 769583

Lennard Publishing
The Old School
Brewhouse Hill
Wheathampstead
Herts AL4 8AN

Tel: 0235 835001
Fax: 0235 832068

Lyonbooks
1 The Mews
86A Cavendish Place
Eastbourne
East Sussex BN21 3RR

Magna Books
Harvey's Bookshop Ltd.
Magna Road
Wigston
Leicester LE8 2ZH

Manchester University Press
Oxford Road
Manchester M13 9PL

Contact: Catherine Whelan

Tel: 061 273 5539
Fax: 061 274 3346

Publisher with thriving list in military studies including 'War Armed Forces and Society' series and their new series 'Manchester History of the British Army'. A listing of all titles is available on request.

Merlin Milbooks
72 Spencers Road
Horsham
West Sussex RH12 2JG

Tel: 0403 57626

Midland Counties Publications
Unit 3 Maizefield
Hinkley Fields
Hinkley
Leics LE10 1YF

Tel: 0455 233747
Fax: 0458 841805

Publishers and distributors of aviation, military, railway, spaceflight and astronomy books, magazines and videos. Large selections of titles in stock for mail order worldwide. Free illustrated catalogues on request. Also second hand/out-of-print

search service. Visitors welcome although are requested to phone first.

Navwar
11 Electric Parade
Seven Kings Road
Ilford
Essex IG3 8BY

Contact: William McKenzie

Tel: 081 590 6731
Fax: 081 590 6731

Manufacturers of 1/1200th and 1/3000th ships, Naismith Design, Roundway Miniatures and Heroics and Ros Figures, Publishers. Complete selection of Osprey, wargame rules, paint and action zoo. Mail order specialists. Trade enquiries welcome. Open Mon–Sat (except Thurs), 9.00am–5.30pm.

Norlon Publishing
65 Ermine Side
Enfield EN1 1DO
Fax: 01144 1 807 6755

Octopus Publishing Group
Michelin House
81 Fulham Road
London SW3 6RB

Tel: 071 581 9393
Fax: 071 589 8419

Osprey Publishing Ltd
59 Grosvenor Street
London W1X 9DA

Tel: 071 493 5841
Fax: 071 491 3803

Oxford University Press
Walton Street
Oxford OX2 6DP

Tel: 0865 56767
Fax: 0865 56646

International publishing house with titles on strategic studies, war studies, peace studies, current affairs and political economy. Also distribute titles on behalf of the Stockholm International Peace Research Institute – including SPRI Yearbook, reviewing developments in nuclear weapons, world military expenditure and international arms trade.

PSL
Thorsons Publishing Group
Denington Estate
Wellingborough
Northants NN8 2RQ

Partizan Press
26 Cliffsea Grove
Leigh–On–Sea
Essex SS9 1NQ

Contact: David Ryan

Tel: 0702 73986

Producers of books on all military subjects, specialising in the Seventeenth century. Also publish 'English Civil War Notes & Queries'; 'Eighteenth Century Military Notes & Queries'; and 'Napoleonic Notes & Queries' magazines.

Pathfinder Press
47 The Cut
London SE1 8LL

Tel: 071 261 1354

Patrick Stephens Ltd.
Sparkford
Nr Yeovil
Somerset BA22 7JJ

Contact: Darryl Reach

Tel: 0963 40635
Fax: 0963 40023

Publishers of military, model making and war gaming books for enthusiasts. Free catalogue on request. Suggestions for new books always welcome.

Paul H. Crompton Ltd.
638 Fulham Road
London SW6 5RT

Tel: 071 788 9130

Pergamon Press
Headington Hill Hall
Oxford OX3 0BW

Tel: 0865 64881

Picton Publishing Ltd.
Queensbridge Cottages
Patterdown
Chippenham
Wiltshire SN15 2NS

Contact: David Picton-Phillips

Tel: 0249 443430
Fax: 0249 443024

Publishers of military and local history. Mail order of new and second hand books. Fine art prints. Catalogue by request with a 50p stamp. Office hours 10.00am–5.00pm. 24hr Fax. No callers. Visa, Access.

Pitkin Pictorials Ltd.
North Way
Andover
Hants SP10 5BE

Tel: 0264 332424
Fax: 0264 64418

Queen's Own Highlanders Reg. Museum
Fort George
Ardersier
Inverness

Tel: 0463 224380

Exhibits from Seaforth, Camerons, Lovat Scouts. Publishers of Regimental history. Pipe music, piping history. Shop and mail order. Books, postcards, prints, tapes etc. Open April–Sept Mon–Fri 10.00am–6.00pm, Sun 2.00pm–6.00pm, October–March, Mon–Fri 10.00am–4.00pm.

Ray Westlake Military Books
53 Claremont
Malpas
Newport
Gwent NP9 6PL

Contact: Ray Westlake

Tel: 0633 854135
Fax: 0633 854135

A mail order book firm offering a service to historians, collectors and modellers. Holding more than 5,000 new and second hand military books in stock they are able to dispatch orders within 24 hours or receipt. Orders can be taken by post or telephone (8.00am–8.00pm including weekends). Quarterly lists are published – send £1.00 in stamps. The Ray Westlake Unit Archives hold files dealing with the histories, uniforms, badges and organisation of some 6,000 units of the British army. Inexpensive research can be undertaken and slides or prints of over 20,000 items provided.

Redoubt Books
95 Downsview Road
St. Helens
Ryde
Isle of Wight PO33 1YD

Robert Hale Ltd.
Clerkenwell House
Clerkenwell Green
London EC1R 0HT

Tel: 071 251 2661

Routledge & Kegan Paul
11 New Fetter Lane
London EC4P 4EE

Tel: 0264 62141

R.J. Leach & Co.
38 Inglemere Road
Forest Hill
London SE23 2BE

Contact: Richard Leach

Tel: 081 699 4946

Publishers on all aspects of military history producing approximately six titles yearly. Reprints and new titles. Mail order. List of titles supplied on request.

SM Books
75 High Road
Bassett
Essex CM16 6HW

Salamander Books Ltd.
129–137 York Way
London N7

Tel: 071 267 4447
Fax: 071 267 5112

Scale Model Accessories Ltd.
160 Green Street
Enfield EN3 7LB

Severn House Publishers Ltd.
40–42 William IV Street
London WC2N 4DF

Tel: 071 240 9683

Shire Publications Ltd.
Cromwell House
Church Street
Princes Risborough, Aylesbury
Bucks HP17 9AJ

Tel: 084 44 4301

Sidgwick & Jackson Ltd.
1 Tavistock Chambers
Bloomsbury Way
London WC1A 2SG

Tel: 071 242 6081

Souvenir Press Ltd.
43 Great Russell Street
London WC1B 3PA

Tel: 071 580 9307

Spa Books & Strong Oak Press
PO Box 47
Stevenage
Herts SG2 8UH

Tel: 0438 310009

Spellmont Ltd.
12 Dene Way
Speldhurst
Nr Tunbridge Wells
Kent TN3 0NX

Contact: Ian Morley–Clarke

Tel: 0892 862860
Fax: 0892 863861

Specialists in illustrated military pictorial histories, focussing on the strategy and tactics of warfare, detailing weaponry and supplies, composition of forces, including allies and personal qualities of commanders in their campaigns, Regimental and Corps histories, biographies and autobiographies.
<NAME>Spink & Son Ltd.
5 King Street
St James's
London SW1Y 6QS

Contact: Andrew Litherland

Tel: 071 930 7888
Fax: 071 839 4853

Extensive stock of orders, decorations and medals. Spinks publish numismatic reference books and a monthly sales list 'The Numismatic Circular'. Regular auctions held and comprehensive medal display service offered. Mon–Fri 9.30am–5.30pm.

Stratagem
18 Lovers lane
Newark
Notts NG24 1HZ

Contact: Duncan McFarlane

Tel: 0636 71973

Terence Wise Military Books
Pantiles
Garth Lane
Knighton
Powys LD7 1HH

Contact: Terence Wise

Specialists in the supply of Regimental and Divisional histories, mostly Britain and Commonwealth, but also for the armies of all major countries. Free catalogues spring and autumn listing over 1,000 titles. The company also publishes reprints of rare military titles, a guide to military museums and rules and titles for wargamers.

The Crowood Press
Crowood House
Ramsbury
Marlborough
Wilts SN8 2HE

Tel: 0672 20320

The London Stamp Exchange Ltd.
5 Buckingham Street
Strand
London WC2N 6BS

The Macmillan Press Ltd.
4 Little Essex Street
London WC2R 3LF

Tel: 071 836 6633
Fax: 071 379 4204

The Mary Rose Trading Co. Ltd.
No. 5 Boathouse
HM Naval Base
Portsmouth
Hants PO1 3PX

The Medals Yearbook
70 Antlers Hill
Chingford
London E4 7RY

Time–Life Books
153 New Bond Street
London
London W1Y 0AA

University of Nebraska Press
1 Gower Street
London WC1 6HA

Tel: 071 580 3994
Fax: 071 580 3995

Unwin Hyman Ltd.
37–39 Queen Elizabeth Street
London SE1 2QB

Tel: 071 407 0709

Viking
27 Wright's Lane
London W8 5TZ

Tel: 071 938 2200
Fax: 071 937 8704

Wessex Military Publishing
PO Box 133
Deal
Kent CT14 9YT

Contact: Mike Chappell

Tel: 0304 369652
Fax: 0304 361268

Publishers of Mike Chappell's series 'The British Soldier in the 20th Century'. Brochures, order forms and trade terms are available post–free from Wessex. Booklets £4.95 each.

Windrow & Greene
5 Gerrard Street
London W1V 7LJ

Tel: 071 287 4570
Fax: 071 494 3869

Publishers of a wide range of high quality books for the military enthusiast, including the Europa Militaria series. Catalogue available free on request. Mail order service.

EUROPA MILITARIA SERIES

Windrow & Greene PUBLISHING

Write for a free list to:
**Windrow & Greene,
5 Gerrard Street,
London W1V 7LJ**

A superbly produced, full-colour, photographic series, which has been acclaimed by experts and enthusiasts around the world. Wide ranging, in-depth coverage of specific military subjects with photographic detail, often never seen before, as well as an expertly written text to guide the reader.

EUROPA-MILITARIA ALREADY PUBLISHED:
260×195mm, 64 pages, full-colour photographs throughout, paperback

EUROPA MILITARIA 1
**PARAS: FRENCH PARATROOPS TODAY –
11e DIVISION PARACHUTISTE**
Yves Debay
The elite paratroop units of France's airborne division are illustrated in training, on manoeuvres, and on active service overseas. Text, photos and diagrams give a clear breakdown of all the units: their organisation, insignia, personal and support weapons, and missions in Europe and overseas.
ISBN 1 872004 05 9   **£9.95**

EUROPA MILITARIA 2
WORLD WAR II INFANTRY IN COLOUR PHOTOGRAPHS
Laurent Mirouze
A unique study of the uniforms, insignia, personal equipment and weapons of the fighting men of all major armies of World War II. Rare, all-original uniforms and equipment are modelled 'on the man' and photographed from different angles in full colour. Each example is accompanied by a full text commentary identifying the items illustrated.
ISBN 1 872004 15 6   **£9.95**

EUROPA MILITARIA 3
WORLD WAR I INFANTRY IN COLOUR PHOTOGRAPHS
Laurent Mirouze
A companion volume, offering uniquely detailed photographs of the now very rare surviving original uniforms, equipment and weapons of the fighting men of all major armies of 1914-18, posed and photographed exactly as they were worn in the trenches.
ISBN 1 872004 25 3   **£9.95**

EUROPA MILITARIA 4
ALLIED BATTLE TANKS: WESTERN TANK UNITS ON THE CENTRAL EUROPEAN FRONTIER
Yves Debay
An all-colour photographic record of all major tank formations of NATO's American and European armies as actually employed 'in the field' on operational exercises. Many rare and previously unpublished colour photos of field camouflage and stowage, in front line conditions from the Arctic to the baking plains of southern Europe.
ISBN 1 872004 35 0   **£9.95**

EUROPA MILITARIA 5
US MARINE CORPS IN COLOUR PHOTOGRAPHS
Yves Debay
A striking all-colour photo-essay on the men, the equipment, and the missions of one of the world's most famous military corps. The US Marines represent the ideal of the type of mobile, self-contained, quick reaction force which will be of ever greater importance. This book is an exciting record of the world's most lavishly equipped, versatile, battle-proven, all-arms force of professional warriors.
ISBN 1 872004 50 4   **£9.95**

EUROPA MILITARIA 6
WAFFEN-SS UNIFORMS IN COLOUR PHOTOGRAPHS
Andrew Steven & Peter Amodio
Perfect reference material for collectors, modellers and illustrators: actual surviving uniforms, equipment, and small arms of the elite troops of the Third Reich, photographed in colour 'on the men', in convincing outdoor battlefield scenarios. This imaginative format offers the clearest possible guide to the actual appearance of the varied and complex uniforms so prized by collectors.
ISBN 1 872004 61   **£9.95**

EUROPA MILITARIA 7
**OPERATION DESERT SHIELD
The First 90 Days – The Greatest, Fastest, Furthest Allied Military Deployment Since World War II**
Yves Debay and Eric Micheletti
Operation DESERT SHIELD records the astonishing military operation which put some 500,000 troops, airmen and sailors of the United States and allied forces into the deserts and seas of the Middle East. Straight from the front line, 100, all-colour photos of the men and women — their vehicles and equipment, their weapons, their positions, their aircraft and their helicopters. Supported by a concise but fact-packed text.
ISBN 1 872004 01 6   **£9.95**

EUROPA MILITARIA 8
AIR WAR OVER THE GULF
Eric Micheletti
An all-colour photographic record of the five-week air campaign which ensured allied victory. Dramatic photographs of all major aircraft types involved — USAF, USN, USMC; Royal Air Force; French Armee de l'Air; plus Canadian, Italian, Saudi and Kuwaiti types. Detailed narrative text explaining the missions, the tactics, the 'smart' weapons; technical specifications of all major aircraft; full lists of units committed, with photos of insignia.
ISBN 1 872004 21 0   **£9.95**

EUROPA MILITARIA SPECIAL
THE AMERICAN CIVIL WAR RECREATED IN COLOUR PHOTOGRAPHS
David Schiller
The extraordinary dedication of thousands of American Civil War 're-enactment' enthusiasts has made possible this eerily convincing colour photo-essay. Whole regiments of infantry, squadrons of mounted cavalry, and batteries of working cannon camp and manoeuvre over the actual battlefields of the 1860s.
ISBN 1 872004 40 7   **£12.95**

Magazines

After The Battle
Church House
Church Street
London E15 3JA

Tel: 081 534 8833
Fax: 081 555 7567

Publisher of books and magazines that specialise in revisiting the battlefields of World War II and presenting stories through 'then and now' photographic comparisons. 'Wheels and Tracks' magazine covers the history, use, restoration and preservation of military vehicles.

Antenna
Forest Publishing
15 Welland Close, New Road
St. Ives, Huntingdon
Cambs

Tel: 0480 300661
Fax: 0480 62286

Army Medical Services Magazine
Combined Services Publications
PO Box 4
Farnborough
Hants GU14 7LR

Tel: 0252 515891
Fax: 0252 517918

Army Quarterly & Defence Journal
1 West Street
Tavistock
Devon PL19 8DS

Tel: 0822 613577
Fax: 0822 612785

Back Badge
Combined Service Publications
PO Box 4
Farnborough
Hants GU14 7LR

Tel: 0252 515891
Fax: 0252 517918

Beaufort Publishing Ltd.
PO Box 22
Liphook
Hants GU30 7PJ

Tel: 042 876 588

Specialist publishers producing books on castles. The company publish the highly illustrated quarterly journal 'Fortress' (subscription £18 UK, £20 overseas) and a range of new and reprinted books. They also offers a mail-order list of over 120 books on every aspect of the subject, from hillforts to the Atlantic Wall, including imported, foreign-language and hard to find titles. Send for a free 'Fortress' brochure or booklist.

Call To Arms
7 Chapmans Crescent
Chesham
Buckinghamshire HP5 2QU

The Re-enactment Intersociety Newsletter. Subscriber based and solely devoted to re-enactment and the hobby's numerous branches of interest.

Castle
Combined Service Publications
PO Box 4
Farnborough
Hants GU14 7LR

Tel: 0252 515891
Fax: 0252 517918

Coin and Medal News
Token Publishing Ltd.
Crossways Road, Grayshott
Hindhead
Surrey GU26 6HF

Tel: 0428 737242
Fax: 0428 736979

Corps of Drums Society and Journal
Stepaside Cottage
The Pudgell, Great Chishill
Royston
Herts SG8 8SE

Contact: Malcolm Hooson

Tel: 0763 838780

The Corps of Drums Society is for any one who plays drum or fife or who believes it is important to keep this traditional music alive. In Britain, the Army takes the lead with a Corps of Drums in every Battalion of Foot Guards, every Regular Battalion of English and Welsh line and in many TA and Cadet Battalions as well. The Society has a photographic library and takes a keen interest in history. Its magazine 'Drummer's Call' is full of interesting illustrations and information. Music meetings are held in London through the year and the Society sponsors occasional musters or concentrations of drums.

The Society advises the Army and takes a keen interest in music, training methods and material, instruments and uniform – some of which it supplies. Contact the Hon. Secretary for more details.

Crown Imperial
14 Croft Close
Tonbridge
Kent TN10 4LA

Contact: F.Stevens

Eagle Software & First Empire Software
6 Cranmore Drive
Highley
Bridgnorth
Shropshire WV16 6DS

Contact: David Watkins

Tel: 0746 862455

Publishers of Napoleonic computer moderated tabletop wargaming simulation 'Follow the Eagle V', various machine specifications available. Also publishers of the only dedicated Napoleonic gaming magazine, 'First Empire', published monthly. Mail order and trade supplied.

Fighting Forces
Picton Publishing Ltd.
Citadel Works, Bath Road
Chippenham
Wilts SN15 2AB

Tel: 0249 650391
Fax: 0249 443024

Firm & Forester
Combined Services Publications
PO Box 4
Farnborough
Hants GU14 7LR

Tel: 0252 515891
Fax: 0252 517918

Forces News
Mandrake Marketing
25–26 Market Place
Wisbech
Cambridgeshire PE13 1HE

Tel: 0945 5975

Forces Weekly Echo
Combined Services Publications
PO Box 4
Farnborough
Hants GU14 7LR

Tel: 0252 515891

Forum
Forest Publishing
49–55 Fore Street
Ipswich
Suffolk IP4 1JL

Tel: 0473 55069

Gunner
Combined Services Publications
PO Box 4
Farnborough
Hants GU14 7LR

Tel: 0252 515891
Fax: 0252 517918

Historical Breechloading Smallarms Assoc
c/o Imperial War Museum
Lambeth Road
London SE1 6HZ

Tel: 071 735 5270
Fax: 071 416 5374

For serious students or collectors. Publishes an annual journal and approx 4 newsletters a year. Regular monthly meetings in London. Range practices April–October. Active in monitoring legislation affecting smallarms and ammunition. Occasional national or international symposia. Corresponding membership available for non–U.K. residents.

Honourable Artillery Company Journal
Combined Services Publications
PO Box 4
Farnborough
Hants GU14 7LR

Tel: 0252 515891
Fax: 0252 517918

Jet 48
Forest Publishing Ltd
Breckland House, Church Walk
Mildenhall
Suffolk

Tel: 0638 715445

Journal of the Military Historical Soc.
Royal Signals Museum
Blandford Camp
Dorset DT11 8RH

Lioness
Women's Royal Army Corps Assoc
Queen Elizabeth Park
Guildford
Surrey

Tel: 0252 24431 X8583

London Scottish Regimental Gazette
Combined Services Publications
PO Box 4
Farnborough
Hants GU14 7LR

Tel: 0252 515891
Fax: 0252 517918

London Toy Soldier
Yesteryear Publishing Ltd.
PO Box 1804
London N8 9BD

Contact: Chris Fruin

Tel: 081 341 5876
Fax: 081 340 0457

Mars and Minerva
Combined Services Publications
PO Box 4
Farnborough
Hants GU14 7LR

Tel: 0252 515891
Fax: 0252 517918

Medal News
Token Publishing
84 High Street
Honiton
Devon EX14 8JW

Contact: John W. Mussell

Tel: 0404 45414
Fax: 0404 45313

Military Hobbies
A.E. Morgan Publishers Ltd.
9 West Street
Epsom
Surrey KT18 7RL

Contact: Iain Dickie

Tel: 0372 741411
Fax: 0372 744493

Covers various military interests including uniforms, toy soldiers, re-enactment groups, figure painting and modelling. Illustrated in colour with a New Product section and diary of forthcoming events.

Military Illustrated: Past and Present
5 Gerrard Street
London W1V 7LJ

Tel: 071 287 4570
Fax: 071 494 3869

Monthly magazine for the serious enthusiast and student of the history – all periods, and world wide – of uniforms and insignia, units and personalities, equipment and weapons; plus coverage of medals and flags, military art and film, modelling, re-enactment, etc. Leading authorities offer in–depth, annotated articles, illustrated in colour by respected artists. Back issues and binders available. Subscription rates: 12 issues, £30 UK, £50 Europe, $75 US, from: Select Subscriptions Ltd., 5 Riverpark Estate, Billet Lane, Berkhamsted, Herts HP4 1HL.

Editor: Martin Windrow, c/o Windrow and Greene Ltd., 5 Gerrard Street, London W1V 7LJ, UK.

Military Modelling
Argus Specialist Publications
Argus House, Boundary Way
Hemel Hempstead
Hertfordshire HP2 7ST

Contact: Marilyn Benigno

Tel: 0442 66551
Fax: 0442 66998

Magazine for modellers, wargamers and military enthusiasts. Colour illustrations. Published monthly £1.75.

Military Provost Staff Corps Jrnl
Combined Services Publications
PO Box 4
Farnborough
Hants GU14 7LR

Tel: 0252 515891
Fax: 0252 517918

Miniature Armoured Fighting Vehicles Assoc
15 Berwick Avenue
Heaton Mersey
Stockport
Cheshire SK4 3AA

Contact: Tankette

Tel: 061 432 7574

Exists to promote interest in AFV's and their associated equipment. Information is disseminated through Tankette, a bi-monthly magazine containing articles, photos and plans of interest to both historian and model maker. Contact for details of local branches.

Miniature Wargames
A.E. Morgan Publications Ltd.
9 West Street
Epsom
Surrey KT18 7RL

Contact: Iain Dickie

Tel: 0372 741411
Fax: 0372 744493

Covers every aspect of wargaming and is illustrated by colour pictures. Provides a contact point for clubs, future events and advertisers.

Naval Engineers Journal
Shenandoah
West Park
Minehead
Somerset TA24 8AN

Tel: 0643 3628

North West Territorial
DVA
54–55 Hamilton Square
Birkinhead
Wirral L41 6AU

Pegasus
Combined Services Publications
PO Box 4
Farnborough
Hants GU14 7LR

Tel: 0252 515891
Fax: 0252 517918

Queen's Own Highlander
Combined Services Publications
PO Box 4
Farnborough
Hants GU14 7LR

Tel: 0252 515891
Fax: 0252 517918

R & R In Britain
40 Latchmere Road
London SW11

Tel: 071 223 9696

Raids
Terminal House
Shepperton
Middlesex TW17 8AS

Tel: 0932 228950

Royal Air Force News
MOD, Turnstile House
98 High Holborn
London WC1V 6LL

Tel: 071 430 5020

SSAFA News
16–18 Old Queen Street
Westminster
London SW1

Tel: 071 518 1597

Sapper
Geerings of Ashford Ltd.
Cobbs Wood House, Chart Road
Ashford
Kent TN23 1EP

Tel: 0233 3366

Scottish Military Collectors Society
4 Hillside Cottages
Glenboig
Lanarkshire ML5 2QY

The Society exists to encourage the study of Scottish military history and publishes its own illustrated journal, covering the collecting of badges, headdress, uniforms, medals, photographs, postcards, prints, watercolours, equipment, pistols, powderhorns etc. The SMCS has a world-wide membership.

Society for Army Historical Research
National Army Museum
Royal Hospital Road
London SW3 4HT

Contact: Dr Peter Boyden

Tel: 071 730 0717

Founded in 1921 the Society produces a quarterly magazine covering army/Regimental history, military antiquities, dress, arms and equipment. Membership is £12.00 per annum.

Soldier Magazine
Parsons House
Ordnance Road
Aldershot
Hants GU11 2DU

Contact: Chris Horrocks

Tel: 0252 347355
Fax: 0252 347358

Published by the Ministry of Defence, is the official fortnightly magazine of the British Army and circulates worldwide. It is aimed at serving and retired soldiers and their families as well as civilian enthusiasts. It was the only British Service publication with combat reporting teams covering the Gulf War.

See advertisement facing introduction

Southern Skirmish Association Journal
c/o Meadfield Avenue
Langley
Slough
Berks SL3 8HP

Contact: Lawrence Watson

Tel: 0753 810949
Fax: 0753 062828

Founded 1968. American Civil War 'living history' organisation and registered charity specialising in battle re-enactments, 'living history' displays, research and lectures. The Association can also supply museum exhibits. Services include book reviews and advice for media projects. Publishers of 'Skirmisher' a journal of American Civil War articles, published annually and 'Bugle Call' the noticeboard of the Association's activities published every two months. Over 250 events, including those for the Royal Tournament, English Heritage, HMS Warrior, Hertfordshire County Day, Knebworth House, A & M Records and Thames Television have developed experience and expertise. Further details on request.

Spartan Spirit
Forest Publishing
15 Welland Close
St Ives
Cambs

Tel: 0480 300661
Fax: 0480 62286

Tank
Geerings of Ashford Ltd.
Cobbs Wood House, Chart Road
Ashford
Kent TN23 1EP

Tel: 0233 33366

The Fusilier
Combined Services Publications
PO Box 4
Farnborough
Hants GU14 7LR

Tel: 0252 515891
Fax: 0252 517918

The Globe and Laurel
HMS Nelson(W1)
Whale Island
Portsmouth
Hants PO2 8ER

Tel: 0705 651305
Fax: 0705 822351

The Regimental journal of The Royal Marines.

The Green Howards' Gazette
Combined Services Publications
PO Box 4
Farnborough
Hants GU14 7LR

Tel: 0252 515891
Fax: 0252 517918

The Guards Magazine
Treasurers Office
Household Division Funds
Horseguards Parade, Whitehall
London SW1A 2AX

Tel: 071 930 4466 X2499

The Lancashire Lad
Combined Services Publications
PO Box 4
Farnborough
Hants GU14 7LR

Tel: 0252 515891
Fax: 0252 517918

The Men of Harlech
Combined Services Publications
PO Box 4
Farnborough
Hants GU14 7LR

Tel: 0252 515891
Fax: 0252 517928

The Nautical Magazine
Brown, Son and Ferguson Ltd
4–10 Darnley Street
Glasgow G41 2SD

Tel: 041 429 1234

The Naval Review
32 West Street
Chichester
West Sussex PO19 1QS

The Pennant
Officers Pensions Society Ltd.
15 Buckingham Gate
London SW1E 6NS

Tel: 071 834 0853

The RNSTS Journal
Staff Div 10B
Ministry of Defence
Ensleigh
Bath BA1 5AB

Tel: 0225 67371
Fax: 0225 68110

The Royal Artillery Journal
Combined Service Publications
PO Box 4
Farnborough
Hants GU14 7LR

Tel: 0252 515891
Fax: 0252 517918

The Royal Highland Fusilier
Combined Services Publications
PO Box 4
Farnborough
Hants GU14 7LR

Tel: 0252 515891
Fax: 0252 517918

The Royal Signals Journal
Combined Services Publications
PO Box 4
Farnborough
Hants GU14 7LR

Tel: 0252 515891
Fax: 0252 517918

The Silver Bugle
Combined Services Publications
PO Box 4
Farnborough
Hants GU14 7LR

Tel: 0252 515891
Fax: 0252 517918

The Stafford Knot
Combined Services Publications
PO Box 4
Farnborough
Hants GU14 7LR

Tel: 0252 515891
Fax: 0252 517918

The Thin Red Line
Combined Services Publications
PO Box 4
Farnborough
Hants GU14 7LR

Tel: 0252 515891
Fax: 0252 517918

The Thistle
Combined Services Publications
PO Box 4
Farnborough
Hants GU14 7LR

Tel: 0252 515891
Fax: 0252 517918

The White Rose
Combined Services Publications
PO Box 4
Farnborough
Hants GU14 7LR

Tel: 0252 515891
Fax: 0252 517918

The Wire
Combined Service Publications
PO Box 4
Farnborough
Hants GU14 7LR

Tel: 0252 515891
Fax: 0252 517918

Trident
Medway Press Service Ltd.
58 High Street
Maidstone
Kent ME14 1SY

Tel: 0622 682026

Upper Heyford Guardian
Forest Publishing Ltd.
5 The Phelps
Kidlington
Oxford OX5 1SP

Tel: 08675 79130

Victorian Military Society
62 The Links
St Leonards–on–Sea
East Sussex TN38 0UW

Contact: Richard Caie

Tel: 0424 437103

The Society is an international corresponding organisation which fosters and encourages interest in military matters of the period 1837–1914. It is principally concerned with the forces of the British Empire and its colonies but does not exclude those of other countries. Original research is actively encouraged and its results, together with other items of contemporary interest, are published in the quarterly journal 'Soldiers of the Queen'. Matters of immediate interest are circulated in a periodical newsletter called 'Soldiers Small Book'. Book publications are free to members of the Society. The Society's Victorian Military Fair, widely recognised as the leading event in its field, is held annually in London. Specialist study groups offer expert advice in specific campaigns and other related interests such as wargaming. Special publications, available to members at reduced prices, include sponsored books, prints, study guides etc. Annual subscription rates are UK £12, Overseas £14. Visa and Access cards accepted.

Wargames Illustrated
Stratagem Publications Ltd.
18 Lovers Lane
Newark
Notts NH24 1HZ

Contact: Duncan McFarlane

Tel: 0636 71973

Booksellers & Video Sales

Airborne Forces Museum
Browning Barracks
Aldershot
Hants GU11 2BU

Contact: Diana Andrews

Tel: 0252 349619
Fax: 0252 349203

Open daily 10.00am–4.30pm, closed Mondays. Admission £1.25 adults, 60p children, OAP's & ex servicemen. Gift shop. Suitable for disabled. Free parking. Shop list available by post.

Albion Scott Ltd.
51 York Road
Brentford
Middx TW8 0QP

Contact: Wolfgang Ansorge

Tel: 081 847 3404/5
Fax: 081 847 2543

Large selection of modelling and military books. London shops at 137 Westminster Bridge Road, Waterloo and Military Dept, Foyles, Charing Cross Road. Free catalogues and mail order available. Brentford warehouse open to public Mon–Sat, 9.30am–4.00pm.

Aldershot Military History Trust
Evelyn Woods Road
Queens Avenue
Aldershot
Hants GU11 2LG

Andrew Butler Insignia
10 Chatham Street
Kent CT11 7PP

Anglo–German Book Service
44 Cornfield Terrace
St. Leonards–on–Sea
East Sussex TN37 6JD

Contact: Rolf Hinrichs

Tel: 0424 424690

Specialist in military books from, and about, Germany. Agent for German Flugzeug publications. Suppliers of German and Czech plane kits. Large s.a.e. (38p) for booklist.

Argus Books
Eddington Hook Ltd.
406 Vale Road
Tonbridge
Kent TN9 1XR

Arms Fairs
40 Great James Street
Holborn
London WC1N 3HB

Arms and Militaria Bookshop
34 High Street
Southgate
London N14

Athena Books
34 Imperial Crescent
Town Moor
Doncaster
South Yorkshire DN2 5BU

Tel: 0302 322913
Fax: 0302 730531

Large stockist of military history from 3000BC to WW3. Also specialist sections on Wild West and American Civil War. Over 50,000 new and out–of–print books available. Send for free list. Open Mon–Sat, 9.15am–4.45pm.

Aviation Bookshop
656 Holloway Road
London N19 3PD

Beaufort Publishing Ltd.
PO Box 22
Liphook
Hants GU30 7PJ

Tel: 042 876 588

Specialist publishers producing books on castles. The company publish the highly illustrated quarterly journal 'Fortress' (subscription £18 UK, £20 overseas) and a range of new and reprinted books. They also offers a mail–order list of over 120 books on every aspect of the subject, from hillforts to the Atlantic Wall, including imported, foreign–language and hard to find titles. Send for a free 'Fortress' brochure or booklist.

Caliver Books
26 Cliffsea Grove
Leigh–On–Sea
Essex SS9 1NQ

Contact: David Ryan

Tel: 0702 73986

Booksellers dealing in new and second hand for all periods up to 1939. Specialises in seventeenth and eighteenth centuries. Fast and reliable. Importers of U.S. military titles.

Cambridge Stamp Centre
9 Sussex Street
Cambridge
Cambs CB1 4XG

Tel: 0223 63980

Specialists in the sale and production of autographed 'souvenir' and 'first day covers', with particular emphasis on military, Royal Air Force, navy and army. Full details and lists available on request.

Campaign Books Ltd.
138 Victoria Road
Aldershot
Hants

Central Arms Fairs
11 Berwick Close
Warwick
Warwickshire CV34 5UF

Contact: Chris James

Tel: 0926 497340

Organiser of events for arms, medal & militaria collectors at Cheltenham and Winchester with 70–100 stands present. Also produces the Arms Fair Calendar giving details of all major events in the U.K.. 1992 issue £4.50.

Chelifer Books
Todd Close
Curthwaite
Wigton
Cumbria CA7 8BE

Contact: Mike Smith

Tel: 0228 711388

Ancient to modern second hand and antiquarian books. Subjects includes campaigns, unit historia, uniforms, weapons, model soldiers, biographies, medals and militaria. Also buys good quality military books. 'Wants' lists welcome. Visitors by appointment. Send A5 s.a.e. for monthly catalogue.

Classic Models
66 Lowther Street
Carlisle
Cumbria CA3 8DP

Collett, Norman W.
PO Box 235
London SE23 1NS

Contact: Norman Collett

Tel: 081 291 1435

Established 1975, dealing in British and Commonwealth medals and in military books. Postal business only apart from presence at major medal fairs. Regular catalogues issued of both books and medals, with more than 500 items in each. Subscription per annum is £7 for booklists and £8 for medal lists.

Colour Sergeant
75 Melbourne Road
East Ham
London E6 2RU

Dataffile Books
10 White Hart Lane
Wistaston
Crewe
Cheshire CW2 8EX

Contact: Malcolm Bellis

Tel: 0270 663296

Dorking Models
12–13 West Street
Dorking
Surrey RH4 1BL

Contact: Anthony Lawrence

Tel: 0306 881747

Stockists of most ranges of military kits as well as aircraft and ship models. Manufacturers of Mole military miniature white metal conversion kits in 1/35 scale. Mail order a speciality with many special imports from Eastern Europe. Open Mon–Sat (closed Wed), 9.15am–5.30pm.

Duke Marketing Ltd.
PO Box 46
Milbourn House
St Georges Street
Isle of Man

D. Hewins Models & Hobbies
7 East St. Mary's Gate
Grimsby
South Humberside DN31 1LH

Tel: 0472 347088

Stockists of 'Men at Arms' and many other military books and magazines. All makes of plastic kits. Wargaming and fantasy figures, plus other relevant items. General modelling and scenery accessories. Military and fantasy board/ role playing games.

Open Mon–Wed Fri–Sat, 9.00am–5.30pm.

Earldom of Wessex
9 Durleigh Close
Headley Park
Bristol
Avon BS13 7NQ

Contact: J.K. Siddorn

Tel: 0272 646818
Fax: 0272 646818

Recreator of the life and times of the peoples of Western England at the turn of the First Millennium. They have resident specialists who research to the highest standards. Battle re–enactments between Vikings, Saxons and Normans complement the 'living history' exhibit, creating living images of those times.

Endless Models
5 Endless Street
Salisbury
Wilts

Foyles
119/125 Charing Cross Road
London WC2

Front Line Modelling Service
59 Maryport Road
Dearham
Maryport
Cumbria CA15 7EG

Frontispiece
40 Porters Walk
Tobacco Dock, Pennington St
London E1 9SF

Contact: Reginald Beer

Tel: 071 702 1678

See advertisement facing introduction

G & D Marrin
149 Sandgate Road
Folkestone
Kent

Games
50/54 Manchester Street
Liverpool L1 6ER

Games Unlimited
2 Castle Street
Kingston
Surrey

Games World
129 Kings Street
Hammersmith
London W6 9JG

Great War Medals
22 Selborne Road
London N14 7DH

Contact: M.A. Law

Tel: 081 886 4120

Large, regular mail–order listings of WWI medals and books. Purchased or sold on commission. Research services for military and family historians. Customers' specific wants advertised. O.M.R.S. member. Visa/Mastercard facility. Send s.a.e for sample catalogue.

Hartshill Bookshop
439 Hartshill Road
Stoke–on–Trent
Staffs ST4 6AB

Contact: John Green

General bookshop with wide range of second hand military books. Open Mon–Sat, 10.00am–6.00pm.

Hayles, Derek
35 St Marks Road
Maidenhead
Berks SL6 6DJ

Tel: 0628 39535

Postal business from private premises. Callers welcome by appointment. Stock comprises over 5000 books on military history, campaigns, unit histories, personalities, uniforms, vehicles and weapons. Send 50p stamp for quarterly catalogue. 'Wants' lists welcome. Military books bought.

Haynes, Michael
46 Farnaby Road
Bromley
Kent BR1 4BJ

Specialist in books on the American Civil War and American Frontier. Occasional listings on early American, American Revolution, War of 1812, Texas Revolution and US–Mexican War. Mail order only. List free on request. Overseas enquiries welcome.

Hearts of Oak Bookshop
63 High Street
Rochester
Kent

Historical Reproductions
Sussex Farm Museum
Manor Farm
Horam, Nr Heathfield
E.Sussex TN21 0JB

Contact: Roy King

Reproduction armourer, helmets, edged weapons and some associated goods. Theatrical and film props, cannons, siege engines etc. Pyrotechnic service for simulated battles available. Mail order, limited catalogue available – most items made to order. Visitors by appointment only. Surrounding fields and Farm Museum available for location hire.

History Books/Military Books
2 The Broadway
London N11 3DU

Tel: 081 368 8568
Fax: 081 368 8568

Specialist in military history. Large stock of new and second hand books including many imported titles, on uniforms, weapons, unit histories, biographies, battles, campaigns, espionage and terrorism. Annotated catalogues issued each of over 1000 titles, which often includes videos and computer simulations.
1. General military.
2. American military achievement. From the Revolution to the Gulf.
3. German and European Axis World War II Armed Forces.
£1.00 per catalogue. Visa and Mastercard accepted. Visitors welcome between 10.00am–1.00pm Tues to Fri inclusive. The hours are different at Christmas and other public holidays, it is always advisable to telephone prior to calling.

Hoopers
105 Cornwall Street
Plymouth
Devon PL1 1PA

Contact: Brian Mardon

Tel: 0752 667840
Fax: 0752 667840

Model shop and newsagent providing selection of plastic kits, military (including naval) and transport books. Postal service.

Hopkins, Steven
Lincomb House
Lincomb
Stourport–on–Severn
Worcestershire DY13 9RB

Tel: 0299 251336

Specialist dealer in out–of–print military books, especially Victorian campaign histories and memoirs and particularly African wars. Send s.a.e. for catalogue. Visitors by appointment. 'Wants' lists welcomed and items thereon actively pursued. Any new book obtained to order.

ISO Publications
137 Westminster Bridge Road
London SE1 7HR

Tel: 071 261 9588
Fax: 071 261 9179

Ian Allan Ltd.
Terminal House
Shepperton
Middlesex TW17 8AS

Tel: 0932 228950

Publishers of military, aviation and transport subjects, including the 'Collectors Guide, 'At War' and 'ABC' series along with the monthly magazine 'Raids'. Also runs specialist interest bookshops in London and Birmingham and a mail order service through Bookpoint (39 Milton Park, Abingdon, OX14 4TD).

Imperial War Museum
Lambeth Road
London SE1 6HZ

Contact: Linda Hart

Tel: 071 416 5000
Fax: 071 416 5374

A unique institution telling the story of 20th century warfare. It contains exhibitions on the two World Wars, a 'large exhibits' hall, art galleries, a cafe and a shop. Open Mon–Sun 10.00am–6.00pm. Admission adults £3.30, concessions £1.65. Tube Lambeth North, Elephant and Castle. British Rail – Waterloo, Elephant and Castle.

James Stuart Books
P.O. Box 70
Petersfield
Hants GU32 3NG

Tel: 0730 69021

Jones, Graeme
190/4 South Gyle Mains
Edinburgh EH12 9ER

Mail order booksellers specialising in used copies of standard and rare works of military history, biography, theory and practice, covering the period from antiquity to 1918. Catalogue on request. Overseas enquiries I.R.C.

Keegan's Bookshop
Merchant's Place
Friar Street
Reading

Tel: 0734 587253

Ken Trotman Ltd.
Unit 11
Ditton Walk
Cambridge CB5 8QD

Tel: 0223 211030

Landmark
21 The Garstons
Great Bookham
Surrey KT3 6NL

Contact: Douglas Polamm

Tel: 0372 4507805

German/Axis and Allied armed forces of WWII, battles, campaigns, uniforms, equipment, AFV's. Also post–war Vietnam etc. Imported from all over the world. Send s.a.e. for the latest issue of 'Book News' giving details of all new titles. Personal callers by appointment only.

M & T Militaria
The Banks
Banks Lane, Victoria Road
Carlisle
Cumbria CA1 2UA

Contact: Malcolm Bowers

Tel: 0228 31988

Specialists in original Third Reich militaria. Regular mail order catalogue with over 700 items. List subscriptions of £4.00 per year for 4 guaranteed copies.

Mac's Models
133–135 Cannongate
Royal Mile
Edinburgh EH8 8BP

Tel: 031 557 5551

Magazine Madness
6 Broadway
Shifnal
Shropshire TF11 8AZ

Contact: Malcolm Rolling

Tel: 0952 460587

Supplier of back issues of all military modelling magazines. Lists of magazine contents issued. Also second hand books. Mail order. Shop open only Sat 10.00am–5.00pm.

Maggs Bros Ltd.
50 Berkeley Square
London W1X 6EL

Tel: 071 493 7160

Midland Counties Publications
Unit 3 Maizefield
Hinkley Fields
Hinkley
Leics LE10 1YF

Tel: 0455 233747
Fax: 0458 841805

Publishers and distributors of aviation, military, railway, spaceflight and astronomy books, magazines and videos. Large selections of titles in stock for mail order worldwide. Free illustrated catalogues on request. Also second hand/out-of-print

search service. Visitors welcome although are requested to phone first.

Military Parade Bookshop
The Parade
Marlborough
Wilts SN8 1NE

Contact: Peter Kent

Tel: 0672 515470

Military warfare from The Crusades to the Gulf. Specialises in Regimental histories, Napoleonic, World War I & World War II. Over 5,000 titles available. Catalogue with s.a.e.. Open Mon-Sat, 10.00am-5.00pm.

Military Subjects Booksellers
2 Locks Road
Locks Heath
Southampton
Hants S03 6NT

Military & Oriental Ltd.
749 Abbeydale Road
Sheffield
Yorks S7 2BG

Tel: 0742 550536

Suppliers of all militaria, military and historical books. Medal replacement service. Military prints. Regimental ties and blazer badges. Restoration of military antiques. Medal research facility. Medal framing service. Rare and quality military

books.

Mil-Slides
106 Seldon Road
South Croydon
Surrey

Miniature Masters
40a Whitegate Road
Southend-on-Sea
Essex SS1 2LQ

Model World
6 The Precinct
West Meads
Bognor Regis
West Sussex

Morgan Book Services
84 Bushwood Road
Kew Gardens
Surrey TW9 3BQ

Contact: Richard Hansen

Tel: 081 948 8119
Fax: 081 332 2786

UK distributors of German World War II titles in English. Over 50 new titles in 1992. Wholesalers with comprehensive mail order system.

Motor Books
33 St Martins Court
London WV2N 4AL

Tel: 071 836 5376
Fax: 071 497 2539

Real specialists in military, maritime, motoring, aviation and railways. Worldwide mail order service, credit cards accepted. Booklists for each specialisation available. Very close to Leicester Square underground station. Large stocks of new books and video cassettes. Open Mon-Fri 9.30am-5.30pm (Thurs to 7.00pm), Sat 10.30am-1.00pm 2.00pm-5.30pm. Branches: 10, Theatre Square, Swindon, SN1 1QN (0793 523170). 241 Holdenhurst Rd, Bournemouth, BH8 8DA (0202 396469). 8 The Roundway, Headington, Oxford OX3 8DH. (0865 66215). Business hours vary.

Museum of the Order of St.John
St. John's Gate
St. John's Lane
London EC1M 4DA

Contact: Amanda Devonshire

Tel: 071 253 6644
Fax: 071 490 8835

Sixteenth century gatehouse containing armour, silver, coins, medals and other objects of the Knights of St. John. Also uniforms, equipment, memorabilia and records of St. John Ambulance and wartime medical services. Mon-Fri 10.00am-5.00pm, Sat 10.00am-4.00pm. Tours of Gatehouse and Norman Crypt Tues, Fri & Sat 11.00am-2.30pm.

Oppenheim Booksellers
7/9 Exhibition Road
South Kensington
London SW7

Tel: 071 584 4143

Opperman, George
Flat 12
110/112 Bath Road
Cheltenham
Glos GL35 7JX

Private collector with large collection to sell. 50,000 lead soldiers, military books and magazines, post and cigarette cards. Send s.a.e. and 3 x 1st class stamps for lists. Mail order only.

Over the Top
34 Imperial Crescent
Town Moor
Doncaster
South Yorkshire DN2 5BU

Photobook Information Service
No 7 Colwall Industrial Estate
Colwall
Malvern
Worcs WR13 5BR

Tel: 0684 40825
Fax: 0684 40103

Picton Publishing Ltd.
Queensbridge Cottages
Patterdown
Chippenham
Wiltshire SN15 2NS

Contact: David Picton-Phillips

Tel: 0249 443430
Fax: 0249 443024

Publishers of military and local history. Mail order of new and second hand books. Fine art prints. Catalogue by request with a 50p stamp. Office hours 10.00am-5.00pm. 24hr Fax. No callers. Visa, Access.

Quatermasters Stores
17-19 West Wycombe
High Wycombe
Bucks HP11 2NF

Ray Westlake Military Books
53 Claremont
Malpas
Newport
Gwent NP9 6PL

Contact: Ray Westlake

Tel: 0633 854135
Fax: 0633 854135

A mail order book firm offering a service to historians, collectors and modellers. Holding more than 5,000 new and second hand military books in stock they are able to dispatch orders within 24 hours or receipt. Orders can be taken by post or telephone (8.00am–8.00pm including weekends). Quarterly lists are published – send £1.00 in stamps. The Ray Westlake Unit Archives hold files dealing with the histories, uniforms, badges and organisation of some 6,000 units of the British army. Inexpensive research can be undertaken and slides or prints of over 20,000 items provided.

Robb's Bookshop
207–8 Moulsham Street
Chelmsford
Essex CM2 0LG

Royal Air Force Museum
Grahame Park Way
Hendon
London NW9 5LL

Tel: 081 205 2266
Fax: 081 200 1751

National Museum of Aviation with nearly seventy aircraft. Also collections of fine art, arms and armanent, equipment, uniforms and insignia of The Royal Air Force, its predecessors and the airforces of other nations. There is also an extensive library.

Royal Armouries
H.M. Tower of London
London EC3 4AB

Tel: 071 480 6358

The Royal Armouries, HM Tower of London, is the national museum of arms and armour. The collection includes pieces from the Dark Ages to the present day including sporting armours of Henry VIII and Charles I, a hunting and sporting collection, an oriental armoury and an extensive British military 18th & 19th century collection. Admission with Tower ticket. Open Mar–Oct, Mon–Sat 9.30am–5.45.pm, Sun 2.00pm–5.30pm; Nov–Feb Mon–Sat 9.30am–4.30pm, closed Sun. Underground Circle and District to Tower Hill. Bus 15, 42, 78. Riverboat to Tower Pier. Shop, mail order for specialist books and videos, arms and armour replicas, catalogue and newsletter for products and adult education courses available.

Royal Marines Museum
Southsea
Portsmouth
Hampshire PO4 9PX

Tel: 0705 819385/831679
Fax: 0705 838420

The history of the Marines since 1664 to the present day, incorporating medal, uniform and weapon collections. Library and archive research facilities available by appointment. Photographic library with copying service. Museum shop with mail order department. Open Mon–Sun, 10am–4.40pm.

Soldier of Fortune
Unit 3a–b Brymau 3 Estate
River Lane, Saltney
Chester CH4 8RQ

Contact: Peter Kabluczenko

Tel: 0244 681090
Fax: 0244 674651

Specialising in U.S. Forces – modern and Vietnam – clothing and equipment. Also stocks British, West and East German, Belgium, Austrian, French and S.W.A.T. equipment, books, replica and deactivated guns, outdoor and survival. 32 page catalogue available at £1.00. Military showroom at Slatney, visit by appointment only. Shops: 56 Lower Bridge St., Chester. 56 Richmond St., Liverpool.

See advertisement in colour section

Solosy, S.
50 Charing Cross Road
London WC2H

Space City Gifts
33 Marine Terrace
Margate
Kent CT9 1XJ

Tel: 0843 294906

Specialist Book Sales
Unit 3
Belvedere Trading Estate
Taunton
Somerset TA1 3BH

Spink & Son Ltd.
5 King Street
St James's
London SW1Y 6QS

Contact: Andrew Litherland

Tel: 071 930 7888
Fax: 071 839 4853

Extensive stock of orders, decorations and medals. Spinks publish numismatic reference books and a monthly sales list 'The Numismatic Circular'. Regular auctions held and comprehensive medal display service offered. Mon–Fri 9.30am–5.30pm.

Sunset Militaria
Dinedor Cross
Herefordshire HR2 6PF

Contact: David Seeney

Tel: 0432 870 420

Genuine militaria (money back guarantee) headdress, collar badges, titles, formation, trade, foreign badges, buttons, medals, miniature medals, world ribbons, mess badges, special forces, aviation, equipment, uniforms, deactivated weapons, books, photos. Send large s.a.e., stating interests, for sample list (mail order only).

Swansea Models & Hobbies Ltd.
30 Oxford Street
Swansea
West Glamorgan SA1 3AN

Contact: Derek Matthews

Tel: 0792 652877
Fax: 0792 652877

Stockist of military models, figure kits, paints, books, tools and equipment. One of the largest stockists of plastic kits in Wales. Open Mon–Sat, 9.00am–5.30pm. Mail order a speciality. Also stockists of conventional and fantasy wargames.

Terence Wise Military Books
Pantiles
Garth Lane
Knighton
Powys LD7 1HH

Contact: Terence Wise

Specialists in the supply of Regimental and Divisional histories, mostly Britain and Commonwealth, but also for the armies of all major countries. Free catalogues spring and autumn listing over 1,000 titles. The company also publishes reprints of rare military titles, a guide to military museums and rules and titles for wargamers.

The Bookroom
Queen Street
Southwell
Notts NG25

The Bookshelf
No. 3 Town Arms Passage
Bodmin
Cornwall

Tel: 0208 52596

The Collector
36 The Colonnade
Piece Hall
Halifax
West Yorkshire HX1 1RS

Contact: Thomas Wilkinson

Tel: 0422 363895

Large stock of second hand naval, aviation and military books covering all periods. Also second hand magazines. New books ordered. Catalogues issued on specific subject areas. Major credit cards accepted. Open Mon–Sat (closed Thurs) 10.00am–5.30pm, Sun 12.30–4.30pm.

The Colour Sergeant
4 Sandhurst Crescent
Leigh–on–Sea
Essex SS9 4AL

The Games Room
29a Elm Hill
Norwich
Norfolk

The Hobby Shop
17/19 Bold Street
Southport
Merseyside

The Kings Shilling
11–12 Antique City Market
98 Wood Street
London E17

The Mad Colonel
37 Mildmay Park
Islington
London N1 4NA

Contact: Marc St. Clare

Tel: 071 354 3259

Supplier of military items from original sources. Commissions undertaken. Extensive search capability. Large network provides toy soldiers, ship and aircraft models, new and antique dinky toys. All military collectables and curios bought and sold. Write or phone with requirements.

The Norse Film and Pageant Soc
12 Harcourt Drive
Canterbury
Kent CT2 8DP

Contact: Mr M Benstead

The Railway Book & Model Centre
302 Holdenhurst Road
Bournemouth
Dorset DH8 8BX

Tel: 0202 36469

The Railway Book & Model Centre
The Roundway
Headington
Oxford OX3 8DH

Tel: 0865 66215

The Tank Museum
Bovington Camp
Wareham
Dorset BH20 6JG

Contact: George Forty

Tel: 0929 403463
Fax: 0929 405360

Located at Bovington Camp, near Wool (British Rail), Dorset. One of the world's largest and most comprehensive armoured fighting vehicle collections. The library, photographic and plans archive is vast! The shop and mail order service sell a wide range of military books, models and model kits – send s.a.e for details. Open daily 10.00am–5.00pm except 10 days at Christmas. 1992 admission charges:– Adults £4.00, Children/OAP £2.00. Large free coach and car parks, 150 seat licensed self-service restaurant, picnic area and many other features. Regular military events held every year. A must for any modeller, wargamer and military enthusiast!

Toytub
100a Raeburn Place
Edinburgh EH4

Trafalgar Square Collectors Centre
7 Whitcomb Street
London WC2H 7HA

Contact: Raymond Holdich

Tel: 071 930 1979

A selection of British campaign and gallantry medals, British cap badges, Third Reich items, orders, medals and decorations from around the world. Full medal mounting service including court style and framing. Open Mon–Fri, 11.00am–5.30pm.

Ulric of England
6 The Glade
Stoneleigh
Epsom
Surrey KT17 2HB

Tel: 081 393 1434
Fax: 081 393 9555

Third Reich specialist.

Under Two Flags
4 Saint Christopher's Place
London W1M 5HB

Contact: Jack Coutts

Tel: 071 935 6934

Stockist of toy soldiers, model kits, military books, painted figures & dioramas. Open Mon–Sat, 10.00am–5.00pm.

Universal Soldier
10 Old Rectory Close
Instow
Bideford
North Devon EX39 4LY

Vandrad
7 Marpool Hill
Exmouth
Devon EX8 2LJ

Contact: Rick Lawrence

Tel: 0395 278664

Importers of RSM Miniatures and quality wargames figures: 20mm Napoleonic, ACW, Colonial; 25mm SYW, AWI, plus 18th century uniform guides and rules; U.S. and Battle for Empire rules. Also stocks 'Historical Gamer' the U.S. wargames magazine, Rank & File 1859, 1866, 1970–71 15mm figures. Send 3 x 1st class stamps for catalogue.

Victoriana Furnishings
88 Abbey Street
Accrington
Lancs

Victory Supplies
2nd Floor
25 Victoria Street
Liverpool
Merseyside L1 6BD

Tel: 0831 520905

Stockists of coins, medals and banknotes, badges, buttons, bayonets, swords and military items. Lists issued. Callers welcome Mon–Fri, 10.00am–4.00pm. Situated in Liverpool city centre. All the above bought for cash.

See advertisement facing introduction

Warrior Videos
38 Southdown Avenue
Brighton
Sussex BN1 6EH

Wessex Military Publishing
PO Box 133
Deal
Kent CT14 9YT

Contact: Mike Chappell

Tel: 0304 369652
Fax: 0304 361268

Publishers of Mike Chappell's series 'The British Soldier in the 20th Century'. Brochures, order forms and trade terms are available post–free from Wessex. Booklets £4.95 each.

Libraries

Adastral House Library
Theobalds Road
London WC1X 8RU

Contact: A.A. Orgill

Tel: 071 430 7515/7110

Admiralty Research Establishmt
Southwell
Portland
Dorset DT5 2JS

Contact: A.E.G. Wilson

Tel: 0305 820381

Airborne Forces Museum
Browning Barracks
Aldershot
Hants GU11 2BU

Contact: Diana Andrews

Tel: 0252 349619
Fax: 0252 349203

Open daily 10.00am–4.30pm, closed Mondays. Admission £1.25 adults, 60p children, OAP's & ex servicemen. Gift shop. Suitable for disabled. Free parking. Shop list available by post.

Britannia Royal Naval College
Dartmouth
Devon TQ6 0HJ

Contact: RJ Kennell

Tel: 080 43 2141 X328

Defence Operational Analysis Establishmt
Broadoaks
Parvis Road
West Byfleet
Surrey KT14 6LY

Contact: R.W. Slaney

Tel: 093 23 41199 X2119

Fort Cumberland/Portsmouth Militaria Soc
c/o 49 Lichfield Road
Portsmouth
Hants PO3 6DD

Contact: David Quinton

Tel: 0705 668981

HQ & museum adjacent to Round Tower, Broad Street, Old Portsmouth. Local and military history, postcards & books. Re–enactment group Fort Cumberland Guard Royal Marines 1835–40 period musket & cannon displays. Drum corps have been featured on TV frequently. Free. Mon 7.30pm–9.30pm, Sunday 2.00pm–5.00pm.

Imperial War Museum
Lambeth Road
London SE1 6HZ

Contact: Linda Hart

Tel: 071 416 5000
Fax: 071 416 5374

A unique institution telling the story of 20th century warfare. It contains exhibitions on the two World Wars, a 'large exhibits' hall, art galleries, a cafe and a shop. Open Mon–Sun 10.00am–6.00pm. Admission adults £3.30, concessions £1.65. Tube Lambeth North, Elephant and Castle. British Rail – Waterloo, Elephant and Castle.

Internat. Inst. for Strategic Studies
23 Tavistock Street
London WC2E 7NQ

Contact: Jane E. Towell

Tel: 071 379 7676

Ministry of Defence Library Services
Old War Office Building
Whitehall
London SW1A 2EU

Contact: J.C. Andrews

Tel: 071 218 0680

Military Scene
6 Hillcrest
Ottery St Mary
Devon EX11 1XY

Contact: Bob Morrison

Tel: 0404 814164

Museum of the Order of St.John
St. John's Gate
St. John's Lane
London EC1M 4DA

Contact: Amanda Devonshire

Tel: 071 253 6644
Fax: 071 490 8835

Sixteenth century gatehouse containing armour, silver, coins, medals and other objects of the Knights of St. John. Also uniforms, equipment, memorabilia and records of St. John Ambulance and wartime medical services. Mon–Fri 10.00am–5.00pm, Sat 10.00am–4.00pm. Tours of Gatehouse and Norman Crypt Tues, Fri & Sat 11.00am–2.30pm.

Naval Historical Library
Empress State Building
Lillie Road
London SW6 1TR

Contact: A.J. Francis

Tel: 071 385 1244 X3246

Prince Consort's Army Library
Knolly's Road
Aldershot
Hants GU11 1PS

Contact: P.H. Vickers

Tel: 0252 24431 X328

Royal Air Force Museum
Grahame Park Way
Hendon
London NW9 5LL

Tel: 081 205 2266
Fax: 081 200 1751

National Museum of Aviation with nearly seventy aircraft. Also collections of fine art, arms and armanent, equipment, uniforms and insignia of The Royal Air Force, its predecessors and the airforces of other nations. There is also an extensive library.

Royal Army Medical College
Millbank
London SW1P 4RJ

Contact: P.R.R. Gibbs

Tel: 071 834 9060 X220

Royal Artillery Inst. Library
Old Royal Academy
Academy Road, Woolwich
London SE18 4DN

Contact: Brig R.J. Lewendon

Tel: 071 856 5533 X2523/4

Royal College Defence Studies
Seaford House
37 Belgrave Square
London SW1X 8NS

Contact: Cmdr TVG Binney

Tel: 071 235 1091 X210

Royal Marines Museum
Southsea
Portsmouth
Hampshire PO4 9PX

Tel: 0705 819385/831679
Fax: 0705 838420

The history of the Marines since 1664 to the present day, incorporating medal, uniform and weapon collections. Library and archive research facilities available by appointment. Photographic library with copying service. Museum shop with mail order department. Open Mon–Sun, 10am–4.40pm.

Royal Military Academy Sandhurst
Central Library
Camberley
Surrey GU15 4PQ

Contact: J.W. Hunt

Tel: 0276 63344 X367

Royal Naval College
Greenwich
London SE10 9NN

Contact: D. Male

Tel: 081 858 2154

Royal Naval Engineering College
The Library
Manadon
Plymouth PL5 3AQ

Contact: J.R.C. Quibell

Tel: 0752 553740 X310

Scottish United Service Museum
The Castle
Edinburgh EH1 2NG

Contact: Stephen Wood

Tel: 031 225 7534
Fax: 031 225 3848

Scotland's national museum of the Armed Services. Collections include a large and comprehensive range of all types of Scottish military antiquities and a large library and archive, available for use by appointment (tel. ext. 404). Open 9.30am–5.30pm. Entrance fee to Castle.

South Lancashire Regiment Museum RHQ QLR
Peninsula Barracks
O'Leary Street
Warrington
Cheshire WA2 7BR

Contact: Lt Colonel EG Bostock

Tel: 0925 33563

Contains artefacts and records of The 40th & 82nd Regiment and Volunteer Services 1717–1881. The South Lancashire Regiment 1881–1958. The Lancashire Regiment 1958–1970. Display includes uniforms, badges, accoutrements, medals and other relics from 1771 onwards. Comprehensive Regimental records, medal rolls and war diaries.

St Giles Court Library
1 St. Giles High Street
London WC2H 8LD

Contact: L.H. Miller

Tel: 071 632 3770/1/2/

Technical Info. Ctr Royal Engineers
Drayton Camp
Barton Stacey
Winchester
Hampshire SO21 3NH

Contact: J.M. Seaman

Tel: 026 472 372 X366

The Tank Museum
Bovington Camp
Wareham
Dorset BH20 6JG

Contact: George Forty

Tel: 0929 403463
Fax: 0929 405360

Located at Bovington Camp, near Wool (British Rail), Dorset. One of the world's largest and most comprehensive armoured fighting vehicle collections. The library, photographic and plans archive is vast! The shop and mail order service sell a wide range of military books, models and model kits – send s.a.e for details. Open daily 10.00am–5.00pm except 10 days at Christmas. 1992 admission charges:– Adults £4.00, Children/OAP £2.00. Large free coach and car parks, 150 seat licensed self-service restaurant, picnic area and many other features. Regular military events held every year. A must for any modeller, wargamer and military enthusiast!

Travel

American Civil War Society
54 Rowland Close
Cinnamon Brow
Warrington
Cheshire WA2 0DQ

Contact: Bill & Lyn Davies

Tel: 0925 818557

American Civil War re-enactments with organised weekends throughout the country. Recreating authentic camp life and battle re-enactments. Individual Regiments and artillery with authentic uniforms and equipment. Family camp available. Grand balls and social events. 'Living history' lectures, school projects. History tours of USA. Videos for sale.

Assegai Safaris
Oakridge
1 Merryhill Close
London E4 7PT

Tel: 0670 366729

Classic Tours
Kent House
87 Regent Street
London W1R 8LS

Tel: 071 734 7971

Earldom of Wessex
9 Durleigh Close
Headley Park
Bristol
Avon BS13 7NQ

Contact: J.K. Siddorn

Tel: 0272 646818
Fax: 0272 646818

Recreator of the life and times of the peoples of Western England at the turn of the First Millennium. They have resident specialists who research to the highest standards. Battle re-enactments between Vikings, Saxons and Normans complement the 'living history' exhibit, creating living images of those times.

European Travel House Ltd.
24 Down Street
London W1Y 7DQ

Tel: 071 499 8222

Galina International Battlefield Tours
711 Beverley High Road
Hull HU6 7JN

Tel: 0482 804409

Imperial War Museum
Lambeth Road
London SE1 6HZ

Contact: Linda Hart

Tel: 071 416 5000
Fax: 071 416 5374

A unique institution telling the story of 20th century warfare. It contains exhibitions on the two World Wars, a 'large exhibits' hall, art galleries, a cafe and a shop. Open Mon–Sun 10.00am–6.00pm. Admission adults £3.30, concessions £1.65. Tube Lambeth North, Elephant and Castle. British Rail – Waterloo, Elephant and Castle.

Major & Mrs Holt's Battlefield Tours Ltd
15 Market Street
Sandwich
Kent CT13 9DA

Contact: Valmai Holt

Tel: 0304 612248
Fax: 0304 614930

Over 60 tours – WWI, WWII, Napoleonic, US Civil War, US Indian Wars, Crimea, Vietnam, Falklands. All fully commented with guides. Fully bonded. Send for free brochure.

Orientours Ltd.
Kent House
87 Regent Street
London W1R 8LS

Tel: 071 734 7971

Roberts Battlefield Tours
7 Titan House
Calleva Park, Aldermaston
Reading
Berkshire RG7 4QW

Tel: 0734 819973

Battlefield tours organised to France, Belgium, Turkey, South Africa and India on a regular basis.

See advertisement facing contents page

Sar Travel Ltd.
5th Floor
266 Regent Street
London W1R 5DA

Tel: 071 839 2764

Military Vehicles

After The Battle
Church House
Church Street
London E15 3JA

Tel: 081 534 8833
Fax: 081 555 7567

Publisher of books and magazines that specialise in revisiting the battlefields of World War II and presenting stories through 'then and now' photographic comparisons. 'Wheels and Tracks' magazine covers the history, use, restoration and preservation of military vehicles.

Cobbaton Combat Collection
Chittlehampton
Umberleigh
North Devon EX37 9SO

Contact: Preston Issac

Tel: 0769 540740
Fax: 0769 540740

Private collection of over 50 vehicles. Tanks, carriers, A.F.V's, trucks, gun tractors, artillery. Radios, weapons and thousands of smaller items from WWII British, Canadian and Warsaw Pact. Also seperate 'Home Front' building shop selling militaria, deactivated weapons and models. Open April–Oct 7 days, winter Mon–Fri. Adults £2.50, children £1.25.

Invicta Military Vehicle Preservation Soc
c/o Maple Manor Cottage
30 Woodhatch Road
Redhill
Surrey RH1 5JH

Tel: 0737 769907

Society with over 450 members involved in the preservation of military vehicles of all types and ages. Monthly meetings and newsletter with quarterly magazine.

Military Scene
6 Hillcrest
Ottery St Mary
Devon EX11 1XY

Contact: Bob Morrison

Tel: 0404 814164

Military Vehicle Trust
Military Vehicle Conservation Group
P.O. Box 6
Fleet
Hampshire GU13 9PE

Illustrators & Artists

Anderson, Douglas
37 Hyndland Road
Glasgow G12 9UY

Tel: 041 339 8381

Professional artist specialising in drawings and paintings (most media) of military and historic costume, male and female, particularly of Scotland. Wide knowledge of Scottish/Highland Regiments and Highland dress, ancient and modern. Single figures, groups, backgrounds, insignia etc. Work suitable for private and museum display and colour or b/w reproduction.

Chappell, Mike
c/o Wessex Military Publishing
PO Box 133
Deal
Devon CT14 9YT

Tel: 0304 369652

An illustrator of military books for nearly twenty years, Mike Chappell has contributed to more than one hundred publications in that time. His 'British Solider in the 20th Century' series for Wessex is now in its fifth year, building towards a work of substance that will include 96 colour plates, 1,000 photographs and 100,000 words of text. Chappell served for 22 years in the British Army – mostly with the Glosters – retiring as a Regimental Sergeant Major. A 'soldier–artist' in the tradition of A.C. Lovett and A.E. Haswell Miller, his paintings reflect his experience.

Dennis, Peter
'Fieldhead'
The Park
Mansfield
Notts NG18 2AT

Tel: 0623 635219

All military subjects with a particular interest in the American Civil War.

Fosten, Bryan
5 Ross Close
Nyetimber
Nr Bognar Regis
Sussex PO21 3JW

Hannon, Paul
90 Station Road
Kings Langley
Herts WD4 8LB

Hook, Richard & Christa
158 Mill Road
Hailsham
E.Sussex BN27 25H

Lyles, Kevin
24 Victoria Road
Berkhamsted
Herts HP4 2JT

McCouaig, Simon
4 Yeomans Close
Stoke Bishop
Bristol
Avon BS9 1DH

Scollins, R.
14 Ladywood Road
Ilkeston
Derby DE7 4NE

Time Machine (TMAG)
Vern Path
Melplash
Bridport
Dorset DT6 3UD

Contact: Victor Shreeve

Tel: 0308 88470

Victor Shreeve is the English representative of Gerry Embleton's Swiss Company 'Time Machine' TMAG, who make very high quality life–sized 3–D figures for museums and exhbitions. TMAG specializes in accurately costumed historical subjects, 3–D 'Illustrations' with, when required, room settings, perspective backgrounds, scale models and dioramas and all kinds of illustration work. TMAG can research and design displays and has a lot of experience working with museum staff. You can see their work at the National Army Museum in London and in Switzerland at Schloss Lenzburg, Aarau; Kriminal Polizei Museum, Zürich and the Military Museum at Morges, etc. For more information contact Victor Shreeve or direct to Gerry Embleton, TMAG, CH1425 Onnens, Tel: 024 711775, Fax: 024 711945.

See advertisement in colour section

Historical Studies

Crimean War Research Society
4 Castle Estate
Ripponden
Sowerby Bridge
West Yorkshire HX6 4JY

Contact: David Cliff

Tel: 0422 823529

The Society encourages research into every facet of the war, including uniforms, medals and wargames and has a large number of publications with a quarterly journal 'The War Correspondent'.Membership is world-wide and new members welcome.

Mercia Military Society
24 Callendar Close
St. Nicholas Park
Nuneaton
Warwickshire CV11 6LU

Contact: Paddy Griffith

Tel: 0203 350763

Bi-monthly meetings of military history discussion group. £3.00 per year membership.

Military Historical Society
30 Edgeborough Way
Bromley
Kent BR1 2UA

Contact: John Gaylor

Tel: 081 460 7341

Scottish Military Collectors Society
4 Hillside Cottages
Glenboig
Lanarkshire ML5 2QY

The Society exists to encourage the study of Scottish military history and publishes its own illustrated journal, covering the collecting of badges, headdress, uniforms, medals, photographs, postcards, prints, watercolours, equipment, pistols, powderhorns etc. The SMCS has a world-wide membership.

Society for Army Historical Research
National Army Museum
Royal Hospital Road
London SW3 4HT

Contact: Dr Peter Boyden

Tel: 071 730 0717

Founded in 1921 the Society produces a quarterly magazine covering army/ Regimental history, military antiquities, dress, arms and equipment. Membership is £12.00 per annum.

The Commonwealth Forces History Trust
37 Davis Road
Acton
London W3 7SE

Contact: Shamus Wade

Tel: 081 749 1045

Formed to provide a history of the different units of the Defence Forces of the British Commonwealth and Empire from 1066 to 1945 including the American Loyalists and American Indians who fought for the King in the American Revolution. Information on 7,494 Regiments, Corps and Units. Also offer a model soldier consultancy service.

Victorian Military Society
62 The Links
St Leonards-on-Sea
East Sussex TN38 0UW

Contact: Richard Caie

Tel: 0424 437103

The Society is an international corresponding organisation which fosters and encourages interest in military matters of the period 1837-1914. It is principally concerned with the forces of the British Empire and its colonies but does not exclude those of other countries. Original research is actively encouraged and its results, together with other items of contemporary interest, are published in the quarterly journal 'Soldiers of the Queen'. Matters of immediate interest are circulated in a periodical newsletter called 'Soldiers Small Book'. Book publications are free to members of the Society. The Society's Victorian Military Fair, widely recognised as the leading event in its field, is held annually in London. Specialist study groups offer expert advice in specific campaigns and other related interests such as wargaming. Special publications, available to members at reduced prices, include sponsored books, prints, study guides etc. Annual subscription rates are UK £12, Overseas £14. Visa and Access cards accepted.

INDEX

Entries are listed within the section numbers they appear – Entries in bold are advertisers in the directory

Entries are listed within the section numbers they appear   -   Entries in bold are advertisers in the directory

Entries are listed within the section numbers they appear   -   Entries in bold are advertisers in the directory

Make sure of your entry in the next edition of the

UK MILITARIA SOURCEBOOK AND DIRECTORY

PLEASE COMPLETE ALL SECTIONS AND RETURN TO
WINDROW & GREENE, 5 GERRARD STREET, LONDON W1V 7CJ

COMPANY / ORGANISATION DETAILS

First Name _____

Surname _____

Company _____

Address _____

Town _____

County _____ Postcode _____

Telephone _____ Fax _____

MILITARY INTERESTS

Please indicate by ticking the appropriate box(es), which area(s) you are involved in.

☐ Model Shops and Suppliers
☐ Model Makers
☐ Model Equipment and Services
☐ Model Societies
☐ Model Painters
☐ Toy Soldier Makers and Suppliers
☐ Museums
☐ Antiques and Prints
☐ Auction Houses
☐ Uniforms Armour and Insignia
☐ Medals

☐ Re-enactors
☐ Wargames Groups and Suppliers
☐ Wargame Equipment
☐ Publishers
☐ Magazines
☐ Booksellers and Video Sales
☐ Libraries
☐ Travel
☐ Military Vehicles
☐ Illustrators and Artists
☐ Historical Studies

☐ Other Please give description _____

COMPANY / ORGANISATION
INFORMATION

Each entrant is allowed up to 150 words to describe its activities in addition to the name and address. The first 50 WORDS ARE FREE. If you wish to describe your organisation or company more fully, the scale of charges is as follows:
£25 = extra 25 words; £50 = extra 50 words.

Remember that this Directory is intended for practical use so please include all relevant details. So, if you are a museum, opening hours, how to get there, charges, etc; or if a shop some idea of your stock, opening times, do you supply by mail-order, do you have a catalogue or list of stock etc etc. BE AS COMPREHENSIVE AS YOU CAN.

_____

—— Please invoice me on publication.

—— Please send me details of display advertising rates for the next edition of
Windrow & Greene's UK Militaria Directory and Sourcebook.

Name _____

Address _____

_____

_____

Signature _____